A Williamson Little Hands® Book

Around-the-World Art & Activities

Visiting the 7 continents through craft fun

by Judy Press

Illustrations by Betsy Day

Williamson Books  Nashville, Tennessee

ISBN-13: 978-1-885593-45-0
ISBN-10: 1-885593-45-7

Library of Congress Cataloging-in-Publication Data

Press, Judy, 1944-
    Around-the-world art & activities : visiting the 7 continents through craft fun / Judy Press.
        p. cm. — (A Williamson Little Hands book)
    Includes index.
    ISBN-10: 1-885593-45-7 (pbk.)
    1. Activity programs in education—Juvenile literature. 2. Handicraft—Study and teaching—Juvenile literature. 3. Multicultural education—Activity programs—Juvenile literature. I. Title. II. Series.

LB1027.25 .P74 2000
372.5'044—dc21

                                                                00-60030

Little Hands® series editor: **Susan Williamson**
Interior Design: **Nancy-jo Funaro**
Illustrations: **Betsy Day**
Cover design: **Trezzo-Braren Studio**

Published by Williamson Books
An imprint of Ideals Publications
A Guideposts Company
Nashville, Tennessee
www.idealsbooks.com
1-800-586-2572

Printed and bound in the U.S.A.

Wals_Apr10_6

Dedication

To my children

The journey of a thousand miles begins with a single step.
— LAO-TZU

Acknowledgments

I wish to thank the following people for their support and encouragement in the writing of this book: The Mt. Lebanon Public Library; the Carnegie Library of Pittsburgh; Carol Baicker McKee and Andrea Perry; and my husband, Allan, who knows the way without having to ask for directions.

This book would not have been possible without the talent and dedication of the following people at Williamson Publishing: Susan and Jack Williamson, Dana Pierson, Emily Stetson, June Roelle, Vicky Congdon, Jean Silveira, and Merietta McKenzie. A special thanks to designer Nancy-jo Funaro, illustrator Betsy Day, and Ken Braren and Loretta Trezzo at Trezzo-Braren Studio for their creative talents.

Contents

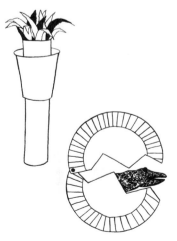

CONTINUED...

A Message to Grown-Ups

On this trip around the world, we'll stop on all seven continents and cross four oceans on an imaginative adventure that will enable children to build a wider view of the world. Our goal is to open kids' eyes to the wonder  of the world by introducing them to continents rather than countries (although we do provide site details).

Every journey starts with a travel plan. Our overall plan is to follow the sunrise, but you can choose your own route.  You might want to begin at home, where kids feel most comfortable. Or you might want to go where you yourself have traveled, to familiar sites that you can describe. Wherever you begin, look at the map on pages 10–11. Trace the route from home to the selected destination. Gather all the supplies you'll need to complete the craft. Then, let the fun begin!

Although specific instructions are provided for each project, always allow the child to make choices and follow his or her own muse. Avoid holding up perfectly completed projects that will only intimidate the young crafter and stifle creativity. Encourage new ideas, fanciful designs, and individualized interpretations so that each piece of art reflects the creativity and mood of the child who made it.

Some of the projects are more challenging to make than others. The globe symbols next to each project will guide you: One globe is the least challenging, and three globes may require more time and help.

Always remember to work in a well-ventilated room, assess your young crafter's propensity to put small objects into his or her mouth (choose materials accordingly), and work with nontoxic materials. Remember that younger siblings may pick up odds and ends from the floor or pull items off the table's edge. When scissors are used, please use child safety scissors, never sharp adult scissors.

When you "reach your destination," send lots of postcards back home. Also pay a visit to your local library and log on to the World Wide Web to learn more about the places you visited. Kids are experts at flights of imagination, which makes them wonderful travelers — real or pretend!

Away We Go!

Hooray! We're off on a journey around the world! Together we'll visit all **seven continents** and cross **four oceans**. We'll travel to different countries to meet a lot of children, share their customs, and learn about their parts of the world.

Kids around the world have different skin colors, different religions, and different interests, and they enjoy different foods. But just like you, they like to play, they like to have pets, and they like to have parties and celebrate holidays. And every one of them is important, just like you!

So let's get ready to travel around the globe to learn about other people and places. We'll learn about some of the areas in which they live, some of the musical instruments they play, and some of the animals that live near them. We'll also explore ancient wonders (like the mysterious statues on Easter Island) and visit modern marvels (like the Eiffel Tower in Paris). We'll see sand dunes in the desert and penguins in the snow. We'll go to museums and monuments, castles and islands. What an adventure!

The route we travel will take us around the globe. You can follow this route, or you can turn to any place or activity that interests you. Use your passport (see page 7) to keep track of the places you visit and your suitcase (see page 8) to hold some of the crafts you make. Remember, our world is not so large. The more we learn about it, the more exciting it is.

Bon voyage! (Have a great trip!)

Miss Judy

Prepare Your Passport

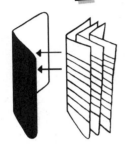

Hi!
I received my passport today! It is like a book with my picture in it. I have to show my passport whenever I enter a new country. When I arrive, someone will stamp it with an official seal and the date. I'll have lots of stamps in my passport when I get home!

Your Friend

PASSPORT

What you need:

- Cereal-box cardboard
- Child safety scissors
- Pencil
- Blue construction paper
- Glue stick
- White paper
- Stapler (for grown-up use only)
- Your photo (ask to use)
- Black marker
- Stars (optional)

What you do:

1. Cut out a 5" x 7" (13 x 18 cm) rectangle from the cardboard. Ask a grown-up to help you trace the cardboard onto blue paper and cut around the traced line.

2. Glue the blue paper onto the cardboard. Fold the cardboard in half as shown.

3. Cut out a 4.5" x 6.5" (11 x 16 cm) rectangle from the cardboard. Trace the cardboard onto white paper three times. Cut out all three pieces and fold them in half the short way.

4. Have a grown-up help you staple the white paper inside the blue cardboard cover. Glue your photo inside the passport. Use the marker to write "Passport" on the front cover. Glue on stars.

Pack a Suitcase

What you need:

- Empty cardboard cereal box
- Child safety scissors
- Scrap of cereal-box cardboard
- Brown paper grocery bag
- Transparent tape
- Masking tape
- 2 paper fasteners*
- Rubber band
- Brown tempera paint, in dish or lid
- Paintbrush
- Decorations (optional)

*Paper fasteners pose a choking and poking danger to young children. Adults should control the supply and insert them into the project.

What you do:

1. Cut around three sides of the cereal box's front panel as shown. Cut out a handle from the scrap cardboard.

2. Wrap the box and the handle in the brown paper. Tape to hold.

3. Use masking tape to attach the handle to the side panel of the box. Loosely attach paper fasteners to the top and front panels of the suitcase.

4. Wrap a rubber band around the paper fasteners to close the suitcase.

5. Decorate your suitcase by painting on brown straps, or adding stickers or pictures of the things you meet in your travels.

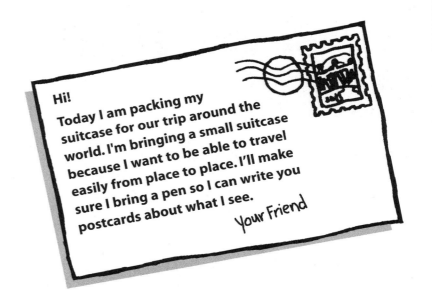

Hi!

Today I am packing my suitcase for our trip around the world. I'm bringing a small suitcase because I want to be able to travel easily from place to place. I'll make sure I bring a pen so I can write you postcards about what I see.

Your Friend

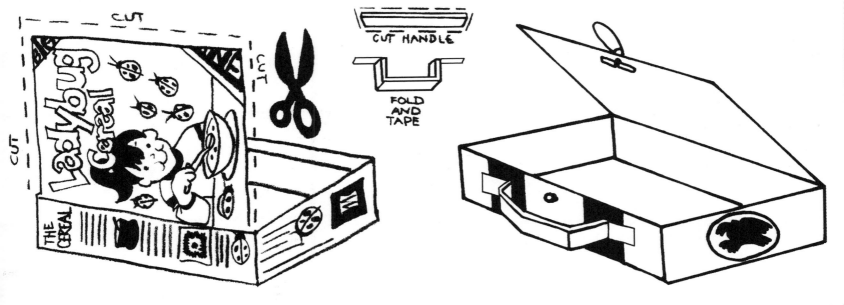

Map of the World

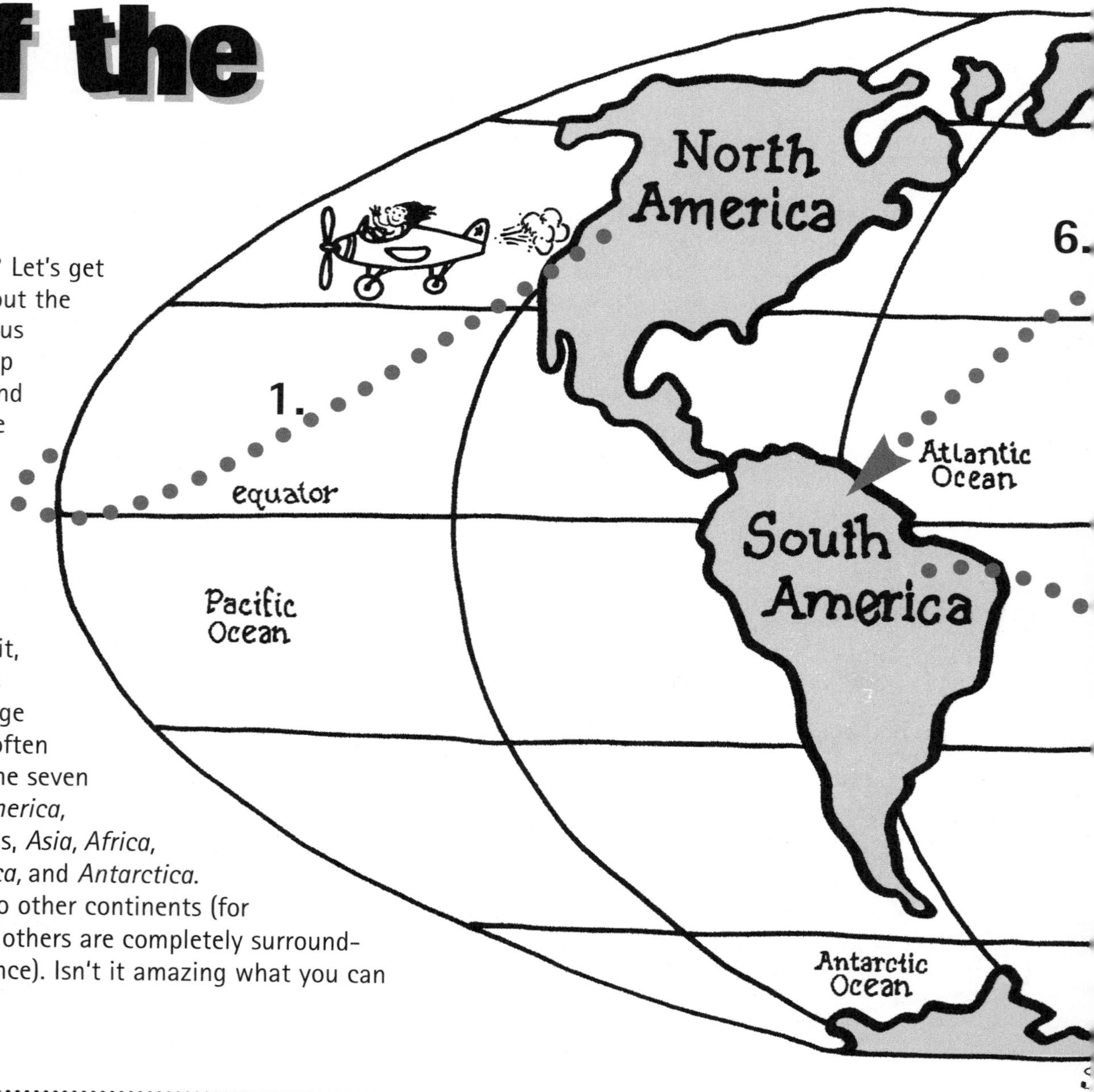

All packed and passport ready? Let's get started on our journey! Throughout the trip, we can use this map to tell us where in the world we are. A map is a picture showing the shape and location of a place as if you were looking down from high in the sky. A map shows you where you are now and where you're going next. A map is a wonderful tool!

Our map will help us find all of the continents we're going to visit, along with the oceans we'll cross to visit them. A *continent* is a huge area of land. Nearby islands are often considered part of a continent. The seven continents on earth are *North America*, *Australia* and many nearby islands, *Asia*, *Africa*, *Europe*, *South* and *Central America*, and *Antarctica*. Some continents are connected to other continents (for example, Asia and Europe), while others are completely surrounded by oceans (Australia, for instance). Isn't it amazing what you can learn from a map?

North America

6.

1.

equator

Atlantic Ocean

South America

Pacific Ocean

Antarctic Ocean

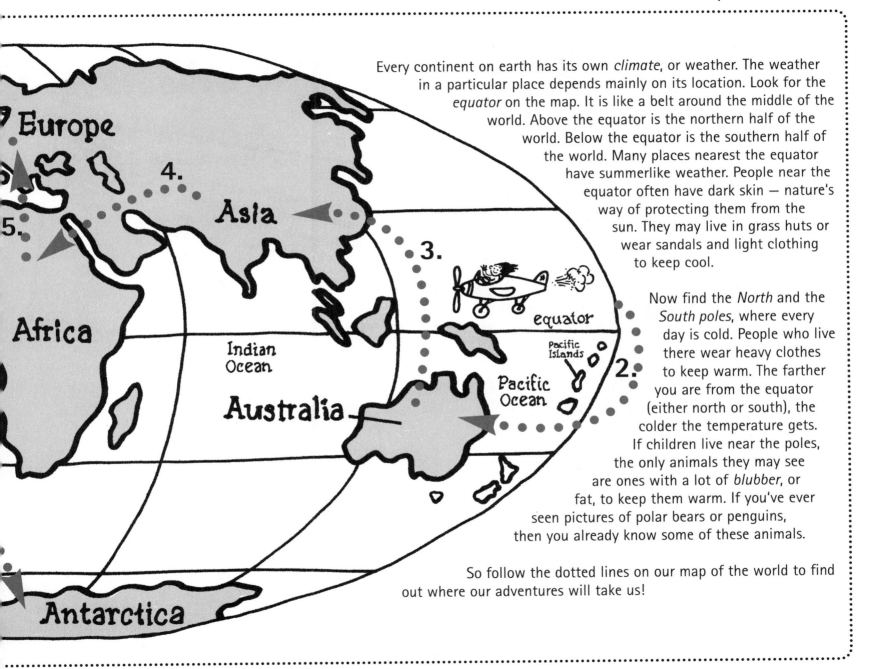

Europe

4.

Asia

5.

Africa

Indian
Ocean

equator

Pacific
Islands

3.

2.

Pacific
Ocean

Australia

Antarctica

Every continent on earth has its own *climate*, or weather. The weather in a particular place depends mainly on its location. Look for the *equator* on the map. It is like a belt around the middle of the world. Above the equator is the northern half of the world. Below the equator is the southern half of the world. Many places nearest the equator have summerlike weather. People near the equator often have dark skin — nature's way of protecting them from the sun. They may live in grass huts or wear sandals and light clothing to keep cool.

Now find the *North* and the *South poles*, where every day is cold. People who live there wear heavy clothes to keep warm. The farther you are from the equator (either north or south), the colder the temperature gets. If children live near the poles, the only animals they may see are ones with a lot of *blubber*, or fat, to keep them warm. If you've ever seen pictures of polar bears or penguins, then you already know some of these animals.

So follow the dotted lines on our map of the world to find out where our adventures will take us!

Save Your Postage Stamps

Hello!

Did you know that every country has its own postage stamps with different designs, colors, and shapes? You can keep the stamps that are sent to you to start a stamp collection!

Your Friend

What you need:

- Cereal-box cardboard
- Child safety scissors
- Pencil
- Assorted construction paper (including white)
- Wavy-edged child safety scissors
- Glue stick
- Markers

What you do:

1. Cut out a 3" x 3 1/2" (7.5 x 8.5 cm) shape from the cardboard. Ask a grown-up to help you trace the cardboard shape onto the white construction paper. Using the wavy-edged scissors, cut out the shapes to make stamps.

2. Cut out a 2" x 2 1/2" (5 x 6 cm) shape from the cardboard. Ask a grown-up to help you trace this cardboard shape onto assorted light-colored paper. Cut them out.

3. Glue a colored piece onto each white, wavy-edged stamp. Use markers to decorate the stamps with boats, flowers, or anything you want.

North America

Welcome to North America! This big continent is named after *Amerigo Vespucci*, an early explorer of the continent. There are three countries on this continent: *Canada* is at the top, *Mexico* is at the bottom, and the *United States* is in the middle. People at the top of North America live near the North Pole, so their weather is often very cold with very long winters. People in southern Canada and the United States live in all sorts of climates. There are cold, snowy mountains and beautiful seashores, and in the U.S., hot, sandy deserts. People in Mexico live near the equator. They have very warm weather, beautiful beaches, and deserts, but high, cool mountains, too.

North America

Statue of Liberty Torch

Hi!
Today I visited this famous statue that welcomes people from across the Atlantic Ocean to the United States in North America! There are steps *inside* her so you can climb to the top — up to the gigantic crown on her forehead. I climbed 354 steps (whew)! I was *tired!*

Your Friend

What you need:

- Child safety scissors
- Paper cup
- Aluminum foil
- Cardboard paper-towel tube
- Green, red, and yellow construction paper
- Transparent tape

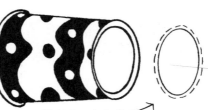

CUT BOTTOM FROM CUP

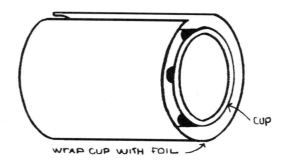

CUP

WRAP CUP WITH FOIL

What you do:

1. Cut away a large circle from the bottom of the paper cup. Wrap the cup in aluminum foil.

2. Wrap the tube in green construction paper. Tape to hold. Slide the tube through the hole in the cup. Tape to hold.

3. Tear strips of yellow and red paper. Tape them around the top of the tube for flames.

Site:
**Ellis Island,
New York City, New York,
United States**

AROUND the WORLD FUN!

⚙ **Make a Statue of Liberty Crown.** Cut out the center of a large paper plate. Glue eight green construction paper triangles around the rim. Now, pose like the real Statue of Liberty!

⚙ **Learn More!** Visit this website to learn more about the Statue of Liberty: **www.endex.com/gf/ buildings/liberty/ liberty.html**

Spirit of St. Louis

Hello!
Charles Lindbergh was the first person to fly a plane from one continent across an ocean to another continent. His plane was called the *Spirit of St. Louis*. He flew it from North America to Europe. His plane is in a museum now, where I saw it hanging from the ceiling. It looked small for such a long trip!   Your Friend

REAR PROPELLER

SPIRIT OF ST.LOUIS

What you need:

- Transparent tape
- Pint (500 ml) milk carton
- Construction paper
- Cereal-box cardboard
- Child safety scissors
- 4 Popsicle sticks
- Marker

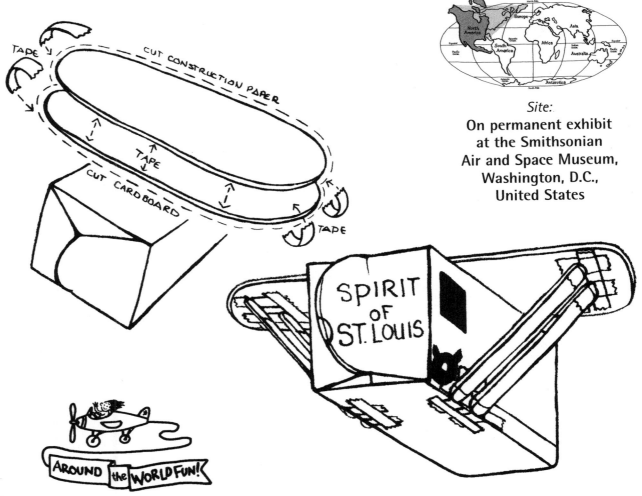

What you do:

1. Tape closed the lid of the milk carton. Wrap the carton in construction paper. Tape to hold.

2. Cut out a piece for the plane's wings from the cardboard. Cover the top of the piece with construction paper. Tape the wings to the top of the carton.

3. Tape the ends of two Popsicle sticks to the underside of one wing and to the carton as shown. Repeat for second wing.

4. Cut out the rear propeller from the cardboard and tape it to the plane. Use the marker to draw the plane's windows, wheels, and front propeller.

AROUND the WORLD FUN!

◉ **Map Talk.** Look at the map on pages 10-11. If Charles Lindbergh flew from North America to Europe, what ocean did he cross? Where in the world would *you* like to fly?

◉ **Talk About It.** Do you have a dream about what you'd like to do when you grow up, like fly an airplane? Tell a story about your dream to a grown-up, who can write it down for you. Then, draw a picture of your dream!

Hatching Alligator

Howdy!

This morning we hiked along a trail in the Everglades. We had to hike in the morning because it is so hot here. I saw a big mound of dirt that turned out to be an alligator's nest. I didn't get too close!

Your Friend

What you need:

- Black construction paper
- Child safety scissors
- Sponge (small piece)
- Yellow tempera paint, in a dish or lid
- Small white paper plate
- Glue stick
- Paper fastener*

Paper fasteners pose a choking and poking danger to young children. Adults should control the supply and insert them into the project.

What you do:

1. Cut out a baby alligator from the black paper. Dab the sponge into the paint. Press it onto the alligator to make a skin design. Let dry.

2. Holding the paper plate upside down, cut a zigzag line across the center. Separate the two halves.

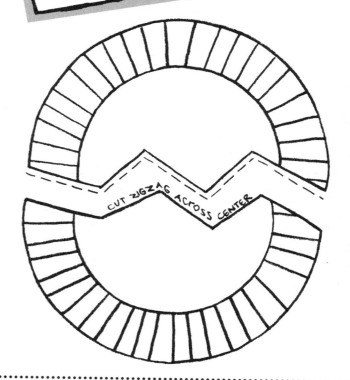

CUT ZIGZAG ACROSS CENTER

3. Glue the alligator inside the lower half of the plate as shown. Use the paper fastener to attach the plate halves together so the halves can be raised and lowered.

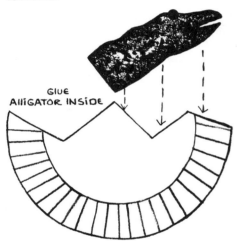

GLUE
ALLIGATOR INSIDE

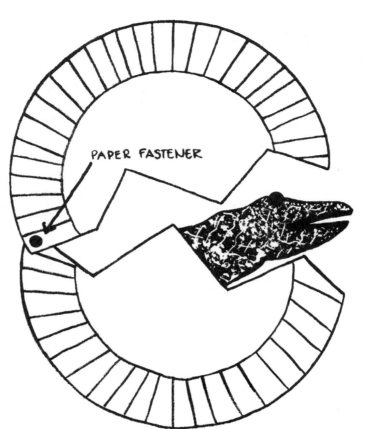

PAPER FASTENER

Site:
Found in the Everglades National Park in southwestern Florida. The Mississippi, or American, alligator is found in the southeastern United States. The Chinese alligator is found in the Yangtze River region of China.

AROUND the WORLD FUN!

⚙ **Camouflage Game.** It's hard to see alligators because their skin is the color of mud and water. That's called *camouflage* — when your color blends into your surroundings. Take a walk with a grown-up and look very carefully at what you see. Do you see anything almost hidden because of its camouflage colors? How about a green bug on a green leaf or a gray squirrel on a gray branch?

⚙ **How Do They Do It?** Do you know how an alligator can see above the water when its body is below the water? Its eyes stick up above its skull! Can you think of other animals that have odd traits that enable them to see, hear, or eat? How about a giraffe that has a long neck to eat leaves in the trees?

The Dinosaur "Sue"

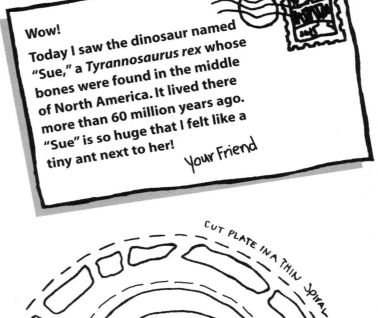

Wow!
Today I saw the dinosaur named "Sue," a *Tyrannosaurus rex* whose bones were found in the middle of North America. It lived there more than 60 million years ago. "Sue" is so huge that I felt like a tiny ant next to her!

Your Friend

What you do:

1. Cut away the rim of the plate. Cut around the plate in a continuous spiral for a thin strip as shown.

2. Cut out dino bones from the spiral strip. Cut out a dino skull from the center of the plate.

3. Glue the bones and skull onto the black paper.

What you need:

- Child safety scissors
- Styrofoam paper plate
- Black construction paper
- White craft glue

CUT PLATE IN A THIN SPIRAL

CUT SKULL FROM CENTER OF PLATE

Site:
**On permanent
exhibit at the
Field Museum in
Chicago, Illinois,
United States**

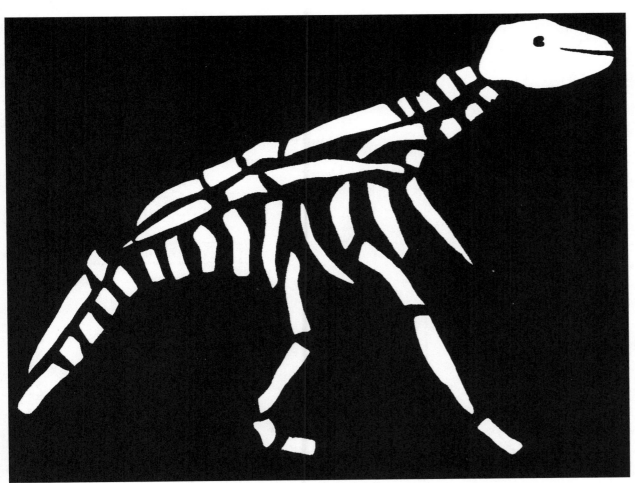

✹ **Learn More!** Check out
this website about Sue:
www.fmnh.org/sue/

✹ **Story Corner.** Read
*The Field Mouse and the
Dinosaur Named Sue*
by Jan Wahl.

Papel Picado

What you need:

- Sheet of tissue paper
- Child safety scissors
- String or yarn
- White craft glue

¡Hola!

A *papel picado* is a colorful paper decoration that hangs like a banner in Mexican marketplaces. Sometimes, many layers of paper are stacked together. Then, many papel picados can be cut at one time. They sure are fun to see and fun to make!

Your Friend

ACCORDION-FOLD PAPER

CUT SHAPES FROM PAPER

What you do:

1. Lay the tissue paper flat. Accordion-fold the paper in 1" (2.5 cm) folds.

2. Cut shapes and designs along the folds 1" (2.5 cm) from the top as shown. Open the paper to see the design.

3. Fold the top edge of the tissue paper over the string and glue to hold. When dry, hang the papel picado from the string.

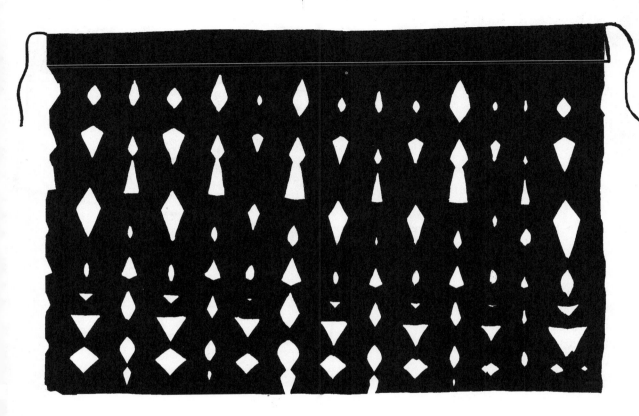

Site:
**Popular throughout
Mexico and wherever
Mexican people live,
such as in the
southwestern
United States**

⚙ **Fiesta Time!** A *fiesta* (a festival) is a time to celebrate with family and friends. Here's an easy recipe for *tacos* (which make a light meal or a snack): Ask a grown-up to brown in a large skillet 1 lb (500 g) of ground beef and a small onion, chopped. Stir in $1/4$ teaspoon (1 ml) cumin, $1/2$ teaspoon (2 ml) oregano, and $1/2$ teaspoon (2 ml) garlic powder. Heat taco shells according to the directions on the package. Spoon about $1/4$ cup (50 ml) of the taco filling into each shell. Top with shredded cheese and lettuce. *Delicioso!*

⚙ **Learn More!** Read the book *Fiesta!* by Ginger Foglesong Guy to learn to count in Spanish.

Giant Sequoia

Hello!

Can you imagine this? I saw a tree so tall that you can't even see the top of it! And its trunk is so wide that you can't reach all the way around it! These trees are called *giant sequoias*. I won't try climbing one of these!

Your Friend

What you need:

- Paper cup
- Child safety scissors
- Brown and green construction paper
- Transparent tape
- Cardboard paper-towel tube
- Brown or black marker

What you do:

1. Cut away a large circle from the bottom of the paper cup. Wrap the cup in brown construction paper and tape to hold.

2. Roll the tube in brown construction paper, leaving 4" (10 cm) hanging over one end. Tape to hold. Cut the paper end into strips as shown and bend them back for the tree's branches.

3. Hold the cup upside down and insert the tube into the hole cut out from the bottom. Use a marker to draw the tree's bark.

4. Cut out leaves from the green construction paper. Tape them onto the branches on top.

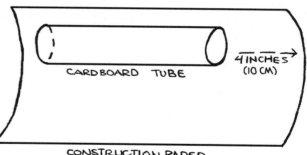

CARDBOARD TUBE

4 INCHES (10 CM)

CONSTRUCTION PAPER

CUT 4 INCHES (10 CM)

Site:
Found in a narrow band along the west coast of North America, from southwestern Oregon to Monterey, California, United States

⚙ **Beautiful Leaves!** Take a walk with a grown-up and point out the different kinds of trees in your neighborhood. Pick up leaves along the way. How many different shapes do you see?

Totem Pole

What you need:

- Cardboard paper-towel tube
- Brown construction paper
- Transparent tape
- Assorted markers
- Child safety scissors
- Cereal-box cardboard

Greetings!
Today I saw real totem poles that the native people carved from trees. Faces and figures are carved on top of one another. Totem poles tell stories about a family. I wish we had a family totem pole. We could tell lots of funny stories!

Your Friend

What you do:

1. Wrap the tube in the brown paper. Tape to hold.

2. Use markers to draw faces and geometric designs on the totem pole.

3. Cut four slits in the bottom of the tube. Cut out four "feet" from the cereal-box cardboard. Slide the "feet" into the slits as shown. Tape to hold.

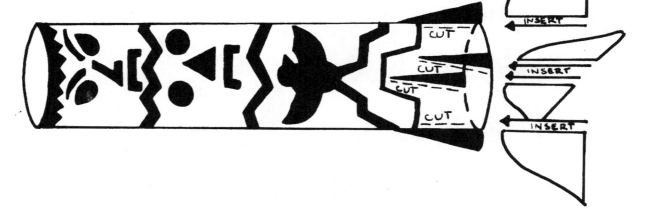

Site:
**Located in
Thunderbird Park,
Victoria,
British Columbia,
Canada. Totem poles
can also be seen
up and down the
northwest coast
of the United States
and Canada.**

AROUND the WORLD FUN!

⚙ **Tell a Family Story.** Make a family totem pole. Draw the people and the places important to you. (If you need more room, use two tubes). When you are done, ask your family and friends if they recognize the story.

⚙ **Tell a Story in Three Ways.** *Draw* a picture, *act* it out (can anyone guess what the story is about?), and then *use words* to tell the story to your family and friends. Is it a happy story or a sad one?

Bald Eagle

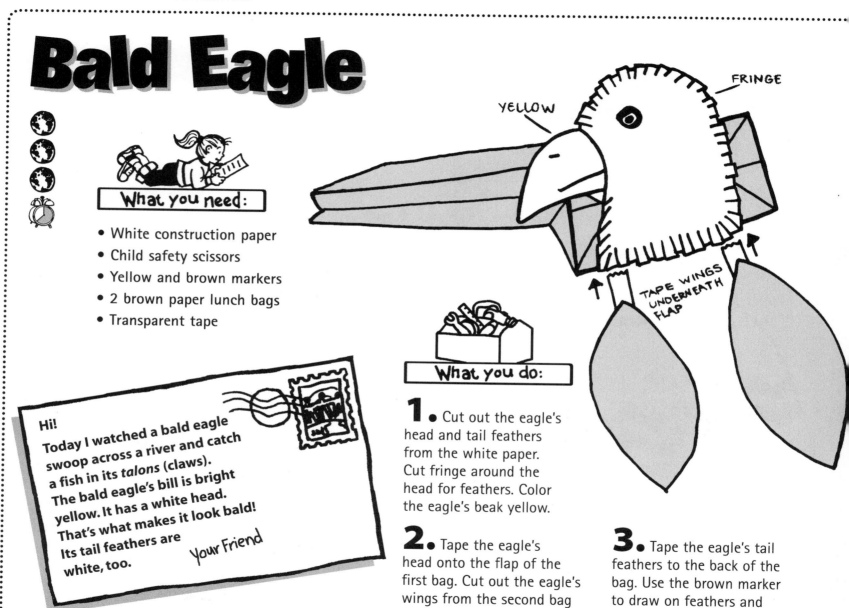

What you need:

- White construction paper
- Child safety scissors
- Yellow and brown markers
- 2 brown paper lunch bags
- Transparent tape

YELLOW

FRINGE

TAPE WINGS UNDERNEATH FLAP

Hi!
Today I watched a bald eagle swoop across a river and catch a fish in its *talons* (claws). The bald eagle's bill is bright yellow. It has a white head. That's what makes it look bald! Its tail feathers are white, too.

Your Friend

What you do:

1. Cut out the eagle's head and tail feathers from the white paper. Cut fringe around the head for feathers. Color the eagle's beak yellow.

2. Tape the eagle's head onto the flap of the first bag. Cut out the eagle's wings from the second bag and tape them underneath the flap as shown.

3. Tape the eagle's tail feathers to the back of the bag. Use the brown marker to draw on feathers and an eye.

TAPE FEATHERS
TO BAG

TAIL FEATHERS

AROUND the WORLD FUN!

Site:
Found only in North America near coastlines, rivers, lakes, and coastal pinelands from Alaska and Canada south into Florida and Baja California

⚙ **Pretend Play.** The bald eagle's wingspan is 7' (2 m). Wow! With wings that big, the eagle can fly gracefully for long periods of time. Your eagle can fly, too! Put your hand inside the bag to make a puppet. Glide gracefully around the room as your eagle floats on air.

⚙ **Learn More!** To learn more about this majestic American bird, check out this website: **www.eagles.org**

The Pacific Islands and Australia

The Pacific Ocean is the largest ocean on the earth, and it is so full of small islands that it's almost impossible to count them all! It's easy to find Australia, though; it is the smallest continent but one of the largest countries on earth! It is between the Pacific and Indian oceans, along with many other island countries. There are lots of strange and funny animals in Australia and the Pacific Islands! Can you think of any that you know about already? If you don't, you're sure to meet some on this trip!

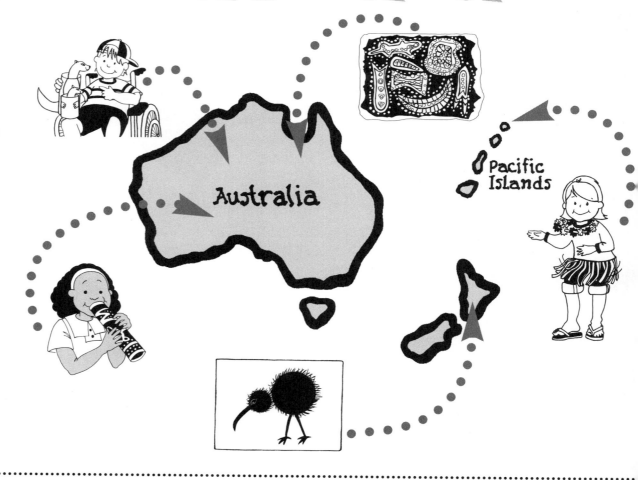

Beautiful Lei

Aloha!
To welcome me to Hawaii, friends put a necklace of flowers, called a lei, around my neck. That's how Hawaiians greet people. They make the necklaces from the beautiful flowers that grow on the islands. I liked the necklace because it was pretty and smelled beautiful.   Your Friend

What you need:

- Assorted construction paper
- Child safety scissors
- Hole punch
- Yarn (enough to make a long necklace)
- Tape
- Tube pasta

What you do:

1. Cut out shapes of flowers from construction paper. Punch a hole in the center of each flower.

2. Put a piece of tape on the yarn end. Thread the flowers onto the yarn, alternating each flower with a piece of pasta. Remove the tape. Tie the ends of the yarn together for a long necklace.

CONTINUED...

Site:
Hawaiian Islands
in
Pacific Ocean

⚙ **Play Meet and Greet.** Around the world there are many different ways to greet people.

- In **North America**, people mostly shake hands.
- In **Europe**, French people often kiss one another on each cheek.
- In **Africa**, Bedouin men stroke their beards.
- In **Africa**, Egyptian people often kiss three times: first on one cheek, then the other, then back to the first cheek.
- In **Asia**, Japanese people often bow to one another.
- In **South America**, Aymara women in Bolivia tip their bowler hats.

Now play Meet and Greet. Greet your family members and friends in some of the ways above. Which way do you like best?

Kiwi Bird

What you need:

- Styrofoam tray (from fruits or vegetables only)
- Child safety scissors
- Cereal-box cardboard
- Tacky glue
- Brown poster paint, in a dish or lid
- Paintbrush
- Light-colored paper
- Brown marker

What you do:

1. From the tray, cut out a small circle for the head and a medium-sized circle for the body. Cut out a long piece for the beak and two straight pieces for the legs.

2. Glue the pieces onto the cardboard to make a kiwi as shown. Allow to dry.

Greetings,

Wow! Today I saw kiwi birds, and they're awesome! And guess what? Kiwi birds of New Zealand have no tails. They have hairlike feathers, but cannot fly. They sleep all day, never drink a drop of water, are nearly blind, and use their nostrils to smell worms buried under the dirt.

Your Friend

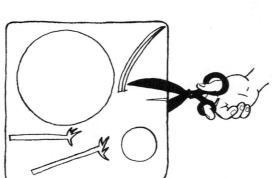

CONTINUED...

3. Brush a thin layer of paint over the Styrofoam bird. Press the paper on top of the painted bird and gently rub. Lift the paper and let the print dry.

4. Use the marker to draw on the kiwi's eyes and feathers.

Site:
The forests of New Zealand

⚙ **Symbols.** The kiwi bird is the national symbol of New Zealand. Can you name the bird that is the national symbol of the United States? If you said the bald eagle (see page 28), you're right!

⚙ **Kiwis!** Sometimes when we hear the word "kiwi," we think of the *kiwifruit*, which is grown in New Zealand. Eat a kiwifruit. Is it sweet or tart?

Aboriginal Bark Painting

What you need:

- Brown paper grocery bag
- Assorted construction paper (including black)
- Glue stick
- Child safety scissors
- Pencil with eraser
- White tempera paint, in a dish or lid
- Black marker

What you do:

1. Cut open the paper bag and lay it flat. Tear a large piece of brown paper from the bag.

2. Tear the black paper in the same shape, slightly smaller than the brown paper. Glue the black paper onto the brown paper.

3. Cut out shapes from the other colors of construction paper. Glue them onto the black paper.

4. Dip the eraser into the paint. Then, press dots on and around the shapes. Use the marker to decorate the shapes.

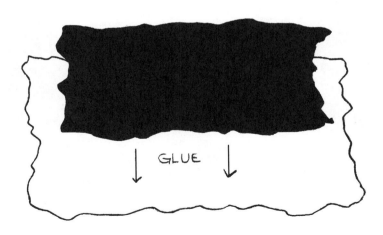

GLUE

CONTINUED...

Site:
**Australia,
home of the
Aborigines,
the native peoples**

✹ **Dream Time.** Use your
bark painting to tell a
story. Your story could be
about a dream you had.
Or tell a story about your
favorite pet, a visit to the
zoo, or fun with your
friends.

Didgeridoo

What you need:

- Cardboard paper-towel tube (for a longer instrument, use a gift-wrap tube)
- White tempera paint, in a dish or lid
- Thin paintbrush

G'day!

We enjoyed a concert of Aboriginal dance and music. We listened to the sound of the didgeridoo. Some people believe it is the world's oldest wind instrument (that's any instrument that you blow into, like a flute)! It's made from parts of the eucalyptus tree. I clapped my hands along with the music. It was so much fun!

Your Friend

What you do:

1. Use white paint to create Aboriginal-like designs on your tube. Allow to dry.

SAMPLE ABORIGINAL DESIGN

SAMPLE ABORIGINAL DESIGN

CONTINUED...

Site:
Australia

⚙ **Play the Didgeridoo.**
Puff out your cheeks and push out your lips. Next, press your lips up against the cardboard-tube didgeridoo and blow air through your lips so they vibrate. You should be making a low-pitched, buzzing sound.

⚙ **Make Music!** Ask a friend to clap two sticks of wood together to accompany your didgeridoo. Now, dance or move to the music!

Kangaroo

G'day!

Hop, hop, hop. That's how the kangaroo I saw today got around. (And I hopped up and down, too!). A baby kangaroo is called a "joey." Every mother kangaroo carries her baby in her pouch. That's how the joey stays warm and dry. What a way to travel!

Your Friend

What you need:

- Brown paper lunch bag
- Child safety scissors
- 1 $\frac{1}{2}$ cardboard toilet-paper tubes
- Transparent tape
- Stapler (for grown-up use only)
- Brown construction paper
- Black marker

What you do:

1. Cut open the paper bag. Wrap the cardboard tubes in the brown paper. Tape to hold.

2. Ask a grown-up to staple the tubes together as shown.

3. Cut out kangaroo heads (one large, one small) and a tail from construction paper. Use the marker to draw on the eyes, nose, and mouth of the mother kangaroo and the joey.

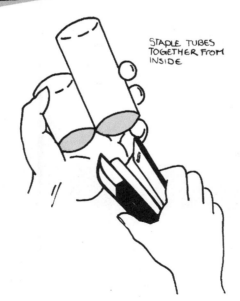

STAPLE TUBES TOGETHER FROM INSIDE

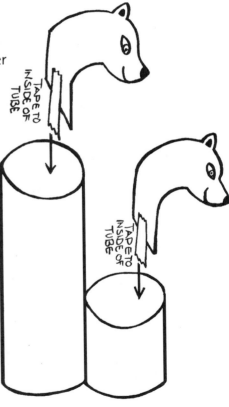

TAPE TO INSIDE OF TUBE

TAPE TO INSIDE OF TUBE

CONTINUED...

4. Tape the large head to the long tube; tape the small head to the short tube. Tape the tail onto the side of the tube. Draw the mother kangaroo's arms around the joey.

Site:
Australia, Tasmania, and New Guinea

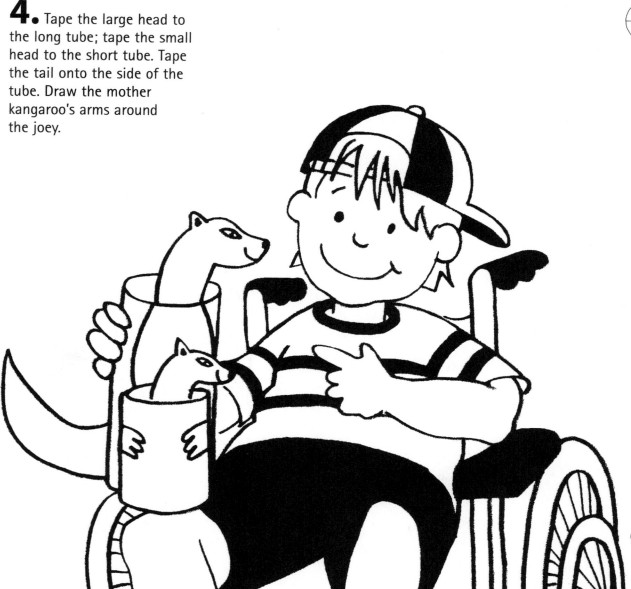

⚙ **"Kangaroo Crossing."** Yes, these signs actually are found on roads in the Australian bush! Make crossing signs by cutting out a triangle from cereal-box cardboard. Use markers to draw a kangaroo on each sign. Put them up around your house and hop by the signs!

⚙ **Story Corner.** Read the book *Katy No Pocket* by Emmy Payne.

Asia

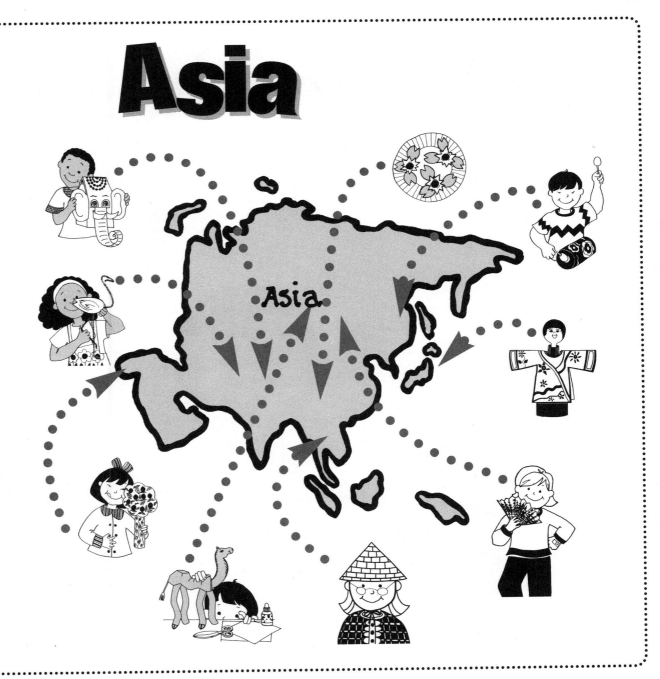

Have you ever heard of *Japan*, *China*, or *India?* They are countries in Asia. People who live in Asia are called Asians. Asia is the world's largest continent on earth! It's also the youngest continent. That means it was the last one to be formed.

And guess what? The highest place on earth and the lowest place on earth are both in Asia! Mount Everest is the highest mountain in the world, and the Dead Sea is the lowest point in the world.

Asia has many islands, which is why it has more coastline than any other continent. Just think of all the beaches you could visit and all the fish you could eat!

Japanese Doll

What you need:

- Cereal-box cardboard
- Child safety scissors
- Pencil
- Assorted construction paper
- Glue stick
- Assorted markers
- Plastic bottle, about 16-oz. (500 ml) size
- Transparent tape

Konichiwa!

I saw so many beautiful dolls today! Parents and daughters celebrate the Doll Festival in Japan. Dolls are displayed on a platform covered with red felt. Many of the dolls are dressed in lovely silk *kimonos* (traditional Japanese clothes) that are made in Asia.

Your Friend

What you do:

1. Cut out the doll's head and long neck from the cardboard. Ask a grown-up to help you trace it onto construction paper two times. Glue the pieces to both sides of the cardboard head. Use markers to draw the doll's face on one side; draw hair on the other side.

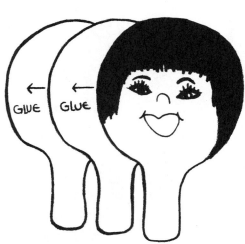

GLUE GLUE

2. Wrap the bottle in construction paper and tape to hold. Pinch the paper together at the neck of the bottle.

3. Fold a piece of construction paper in half and cut out a T shape for the doll's kimono. Use the markers to decorate it. Cut a small slit in the top of the fold, and place the kimono over the neck of the bottle.

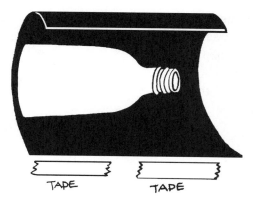

TAPE   TAPE

4. Glue the kimono to the front and back of the bottle and glue the sleeves together. Insert the doll's head into the bottle.

FOLD   SMALL SLIT FOR bottle NECK

GLUE BOTTOM OF THE SLEEVES TOGETHER

GLUE THE KIMONO TO THE FRONT AND BACK OF THE BOTTLE

Site:
Made and displayed in Japan, though other kinds of dolls are found all over the world

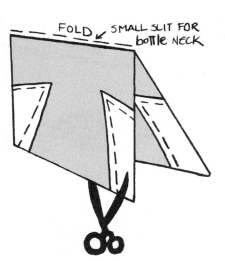

AROUND the WORLD FUN!

⚙ **Gather Flowers.** Japan's Doll Festival is held when the peach blossoms are in bloom. Branches of the blossoms are placed on the display. Gather a bunch of flowers and place them alongside your dolls, Japanese-style.

⚙ **Smooth as Silk!** The making and weaving of silk material began in Asia about 5,000 years ago! Ask a grown-up to show you anything made of silk, like a necktie or a scarf. What does it feel like — smooth, soft, or rough?

⚙ **Special Days.** Japanese children also display their dolls on *Children's Day.* Are there any special days in your country that are planned for children, parents, or grandparents?

Korean Drum

What you need:

- Round cardboard carton with lid (oatmeal, cornmeal, or bread–crumb container)
- Assorted construction paper
- Transparent tape
- Pencil
- Child safety scissors
- Glue stick
- Decorations

Annyong ha shimnikka!

Korean drums lie on their sides so the drummer can hit both ends. The sound of the drum goes *boom, boom, boom.* The one I heard sounded very loud. Sometimes when the drum was too loud I covered my ears with my hands.

Your Friend

What you do:

1. Wrap the carton in construction paper. Tape to hold. Cut off the excess on both ends.

2. Ask a grown-up to help you trace the end of the carton onto the paper two times. Cut out each circle and glue one to each end of the carton.

3. Cut out paper decorations and glue them onto the carton.

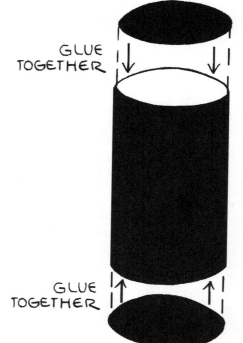

GLUE TOGETHER

GLUE TOGETHER

⚙ **Make Different Sounds**. Korean drummers sometimes use their hands to play their drums, and they also use drumsticks. Play your drum with your fingertips. Then, make a ball out of clay and stick an unsharpened pencil into it. Lay your drum on its side and tap the ends with your clay-and-pencil drumstick. For a tasty drumstick, poke a thin pretzel stick into a marshmallow! Listen to the sound it makes and then eat it up!

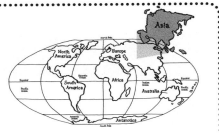

Site:
Specific to Korea and Japan, though many kinds of drums are found on every continent around the world

Bactrian Camel

Ni hao?

I rode a camel today! It was a very bumpy ride. I don't think I'd like to ride all the way across the desert on one! Camels can travel across the desert in Asia because they can survive without water for many days. That's not the life for me — I need food and water many times a day!

Your Friend

What you need:

- Cardboard egg carton
- Child safety scissors
- Cereal-box cardboard
- Brown tempera paint, in a dish or lid
- Paintbrush
- Brown construction paper
- Brown marker
- Tacky glue

What you do:

1. Cut out a two-cup section from the egg carton for the body. Cut out two 1" x 11" (2.5 x 28 cm) strips from the cardboard as shown for the legs.

2. Turn the egg cups upside down and paint them brown. Paint one side of both of the cardboard strips brown. Allow to dry.

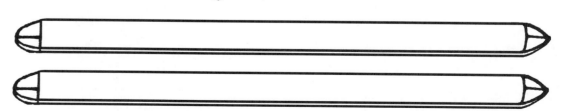

CUT OUT TWO CUPS FROM EGG CARTON

CUT STRIPS OF CARDBOARD FOR LEGS

3. Cut out the camel's head, neck, and tail from the brown paper. Use the marker to draw on the eyes, nose, and mouth.

4. Cut a slit in the end of the egg carton and insert the camel's neck. Glue to hold. Glue on the tail. Bend the legs and glue them into the egg cups. Use the marker to draw on the feet.

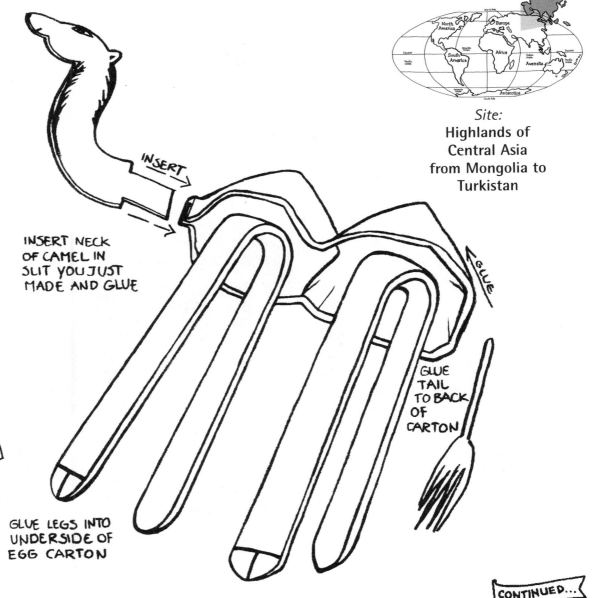

Site:
Highlands of Central Asia from Mongolia to Turkistan

INSERT

INSERT NECK OF CAMEL IN SLIT YOU JUST MADE AND GLUE

GLUE

GLUE TAIL TO BACK OF CARTON

CUT

CUT A SLIT ON SIDE OF CARTON

GLUE LEGS INTO UNDERSIDE OF EGG CARTON

CONTINUED...

AROUND the WORLD FUN!

⚙ **The Better to See You.**
Camels' eyes have double rows of eyelashes. How do you think this helps them when the desert sand blows? What do you do to protect your eyes from the sun?

⚙ **Meet a New Creature.**
Yaks (large, shaggy-haired oxen) are another kind of animal found in Asia. They are very strong and can pull heavy loads. Yaks carry their heads so low that their noses almost touch the ground. How low do you have to bend to touch your nose to the ground? Take a yak-walk around the room.

Chinese Paper Fan

Ni hao?

Today I went to the zoo to see giant pandas. It sure was hot outside! My friend let me use her Chinese fan to cool off. She had a beautiful paper fan with a lovely painting on it. Her brother had a bamboo fan with a design carved in it.

Your Friend

What you need:

- Large piece of white paper
- Assorted markers
- Transparent tape

What you do:

1. Hold the paper so the long side is on the bottom. Use colorful markers to draw a picture on the top half.

2. Turn the paper around and draw a picture on the other half.

CONTINUED...

3. Accordion-fold the paper. Pinch the pleated paper in the center. Bring up the two sides and tape together for a fan.

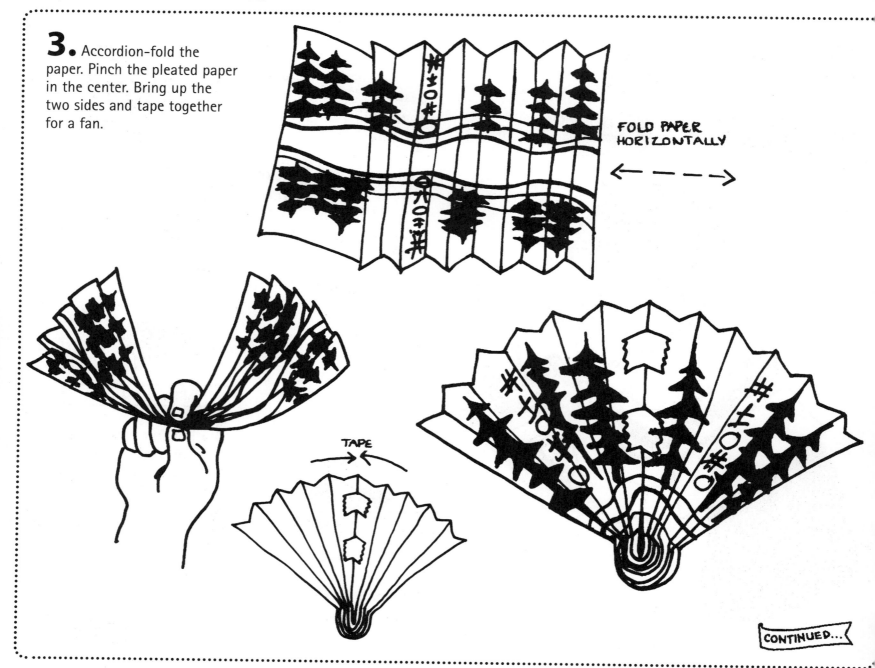

FOLD PAPER HORIZONTALLY

TAPE

CONTINUED...

HOLD FAN FOR EVERYONE TO SEE

AROUND the WORLD FUN!

Site:
Used in China, though all kinds of fans are used all over the world in hot weather

☼ **Keeping Cool.** On hot days in China, both men and women use a paper fan, or *shan*, to cool off. How do you cool off on a hot day? Do you go for a swim? Sit under a leafy tree? Drink glasses of ice-cold lemonade?

☼ **Eating with Sticks.** In many parts of Asia, people eat with chopsticks. Try eating some of your favorite foods with chopsticks. If you don't have chopsticks, use two Popsicle sticks. See how the fingers hold the sticks in the picture? Can you pick up raisins? Strawberries? Spaghetti?

Conical Hat

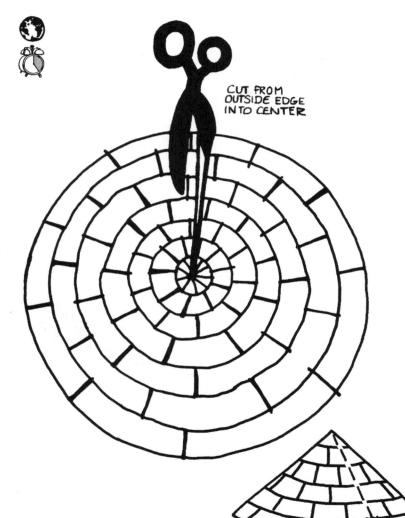

CUT FROM
OUTSIDE EDGE
INTO CENTER

Danh to!

The sun can get very strong and hot here in Asia. I'm wearing a *non la*, a Vietnamese hat that has a point at the top. It ties under my chin and keeps the hot sun off my face.

Your Friend

What you need:

- Brown paper grocery bag
- Child safety scissors
- Brown marker
- Transparent tape
- Yarn

What you do:

1. Cut open the bag and lay it flat. Cut out a 13" (33 cm) wide circle from the bag.

2. Use the marker to draw a woven pattern on the hat.

3. Make a cut from the outside edge of the circle into the center. Overlap the edges to form a peak. Tape the slit ends together.

4. Tape one piece of yarn to each side of the hat to make two ties.

Site:
**Vietnam,
Southeast Asia,
and parts of
southern China**

✵ **Hats for Today!** How many different kinds of hats do you have? Count them up and sort them into winter and summer hats. For fun, take a piece of newspaper and some tape to make yourself a special, one-of-a-kind hat. Then, gather your friends or family, put on hats, and have a parade playing your Korean drum (see page 44).

Lotus Flower

What you need:

- Large white paper plate
- Blue tempera paint, in a dish or lid
- Paintbrush
- Styrofoam egg carton
- Child safety scissors
- Orange and green construction paper
- Tacky glue

Sawasdee!

It's so beautiful here in Asia! I saw yellow, purple, white, pink, and red lotus flowers growing in ponds today. It is a favorite flower in Thailand. In fact, some girls in Asia are named after the lotus blossom.

Your Friend

What you do:

1. Paint the plate blue. Allow to dry.

2. Cut out cups from the egg carton. Cut around the edges to make petals. Glue a dot of orange paper in the center of each flower. Glue the flowers onto the plate.

CUT AROUND EGG CUPS TO FORM PETALS

3. Cut out lotus leaves (see the shape in the illustration) from the green construction paper and glue them onto the plate next to the flowers.

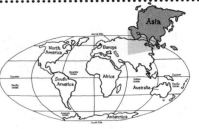

Site:
Found in Thailand and other areas of tropical and subtropical Asia

AROUND the WORLD FUN!

⚙ **Floating Flowers.** Lotus flowers float on top of the water like a lily pad. Try floating your egg-carton lotus flowers in a tub of water. Blow on the flowers to move them around. (Note: Adult supervision is *always* necessary around water — even if it's just a few inches/cm deep!)

⚙ **Name that Food!** In Asia, the roots of the lotus flower are often boiled or preserved in sugar. Its boiled leaves are eaten as a vegetable, and parts of the flower are made into tea. Can you think of foods that you eat that are made from roots, leaves, or flowers?

Indian Elephant

FOLD OVER TOP OF BAG
TAPE SHUT

What you need:

- Brown paper lunch bag
- Old newspapers
- Transparent tape
- Assorted markers
- Wiggly eyes (optional)
- Glue stick
- Brown and white construction paper
- Child safety scissors

Namastay!
Today was the Elephant Festival. The elephants' owners decorated their elephants and marched with them in a parade. The elephants walked very slowly. They are so wonderful and friendly. I love elephants!

Your Friend

What you do:

1. Loosely stuff the bag with crumpled newspapers. Fold over the top of the bag and tape flat.

2. Use a marker to draw the elephant's face onto the bag. Glue on the wiggly eyes.

3. Cut out the elephant's trunk and ears from the brown paper. Cut out the tusks from the white paper.

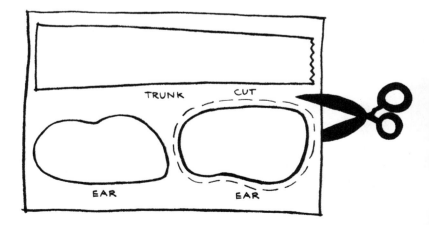

TRUNK   CUT
EAR   EAR

4. Use a marker to outline the ears and trunk. Glue the tusks, trunk, and ears onto the elephant.

AROUND the WORLD FUN!

⚙ **Try this Experiment.** Elephants are smart, hard workers! In India, elephants help workers lift and move logs. Put your hand inside an athletic sock. Practice lifting and moving things with your "trunk." How hard is it to pick up a box of cereal? A basketball? A toy car?

⚙ **Learn More!** Read *Big, Rough, and Wrinkly (What Am I?)* by Moira Butterfield and Wayne Ford.

Site:
Native to the Indian subcontinent and southeastern Asia. The African elephant is found in sub-Saharan Africa.

Flamingo

- Pink construction paper
- Child safety scissors
- 3 white pipe cleaners
- Transparent tape
- Pink marker

Al salaam a'alaykum!

Today I saw flamingos, each standing on one leg. They eat by dipping their heads underwater. Then, they scoop backward with their heads upside down. What a funny way to take a drink of water!

Your Friend

What you do:

1. Fold the pink paper and cut out both sides of the flamingo's body.

2. Twist a pipe cleaner for the flamingo's neck and head. Bend the other two cleaners for the legs. Tape the cleaners on one side of the flamingo's body. Tape the two body pieces together to cover the cleaners.

3. Use the marker to draw the flamingo's feathers.

FOLD

CUT OUT FLAMINGO
BODY FROM PINK PAPER

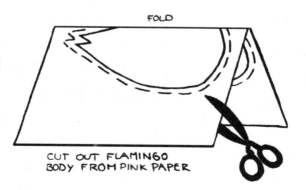

FOLD AND TAPE

TAPE

TAPE

TAPE PIPE CLEANERS
TO INSIDE OF
FLAMINGO

FOLD FLAMINGO BODY
AND TAPE ALONG
BOTTOM

Site:
**Found in tropical
and subtropical
areas around the world.
The greater flamingo
(pale red) is found
in northwest India,
the Middle East,
the western
Mediterranean,
and Africa.
Other types
are found in
South America and
southeastern
North America.**

⚙ **Pretend Play.** Count the seconds you can stand on one leg like a flamingo. Practice and then play a game with your friends to see who can stand flamingo-style the longest.

⚙ **Draw a Pink Picture.** When flamingos fly together, they look like a pink cloud in the sky. Use markers to draw a picture of flamingos in flight, a pink sunset, or silly pink elephants!

Orange Tree

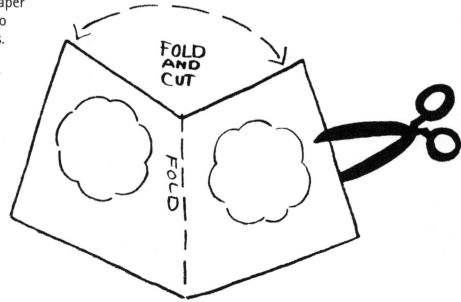

Shalom!

Oranges are my favorite fruit. I like to eat them straight off the tree or squeeze them to make orange juice, too! Here there are many groves where once there was desert. It's so pretty to see the long, long rows of trees being watered by an irrigation system. Your Friend

What you do:

1. Wrap the tube in brown paper. Use the brown marker to draw on the bark for a tree trunk.

2. Fold the green paper in half and cut out two circles for the treetops. Cut out several circles from the orange paper for oranges.

What you need:

- Cardboard paper-towel tube
- Green, brown, and orange construction paper
- Brown and green markers
- Child safety scissors
- Transparent tape
- Glue stick

FOLD AND CUT

FOLD

TAPE BOTH SIDES TOGETHER

TAPE TOGETHER

Site:
Jaffa orange tree found throughout Israel. Sweet and mandarin oranges are grown across the southern United States (in Florida, California, Texas, and Arizona) and in Brazil, China, Spain, Mexico, Italy, India, and Egypt.

3. Tape the two green circles together, with the trunk in the middle. Glue oranges onto the tree.

AROUND the WORLD FUN!

⚙ **Fruit Trees.** How many fruits can you name that grow on trees? On bushes? How about apples, pears, and figs?

⚙ **Plant a Desert Terrarium.** Fill a shallow, terra-cotta pot with planting soil. Plant cactus and other succulent plants. Sprinkle small pebbles over the surface of the soil. Place your terrarium in a sunny window and water sparingly.

Africa

Africa is the second largest continent (Asia, as you know, is the biggest). Africa is so exciting because there are deserts, mountains, beautiful rain forests, and wonderful animals there that don't live anywhere else in the world. Because Africa is divided into almost two equal parts by the equator, most of it is in the tropics, which means that it is very hot for most the year.

And guess what? Many people believe that the name *Africa* came from a very old Latin word meaning "sunny" or from a very old Greek word meaning "without cold." Because the sun shines so much there, nature has given the indigenous African people dark skin to help protect them from sunburn.

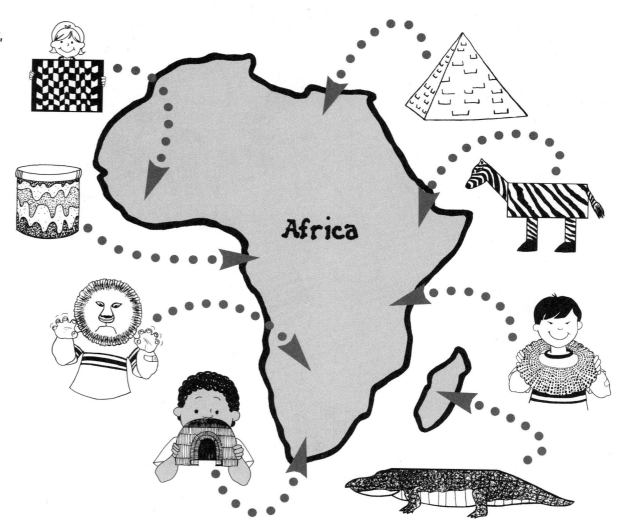

The Great Pyramid

Al salaam a'alaykum!

Today I visited the pyramids of ancient Egypt. Each pyramid is made from stone and has a square base with four triangles for sides. Great Egyptian kings from thousands of years ago, along with their families, pets, servants, and treasures, were buried in the pyramids. They are so huge — I wonder how they were built without heavy machines!

Your Friend

What you need:

- Cereal-box cardboard
- Pencil
- Child safety scissors
- Marker
- Ruler or straightedge
- Transparent tape

What you do:

1. Ask a grown-up to help you trace a 6" (15 cm) square onto the cardboard and cut out the square. Then, ask a grown-up to help you trace four 6" (15 cm) equilateral triangles (all three sides are equal) onto cardboard and cut them out.

TRACE SQUARE ONTO CARDBOARD

6" (15 CM)

CONTINUED...

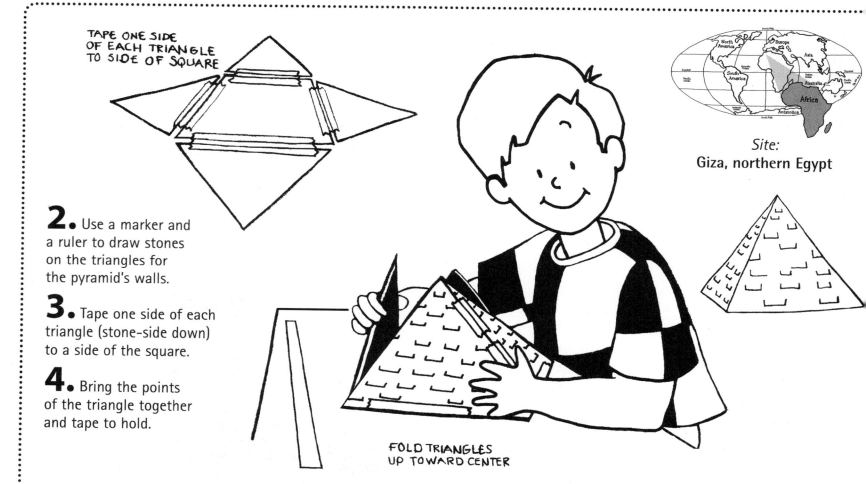

TAPE ONE SIDE OF EACH TRIANGLE TO SIDE OF SQUARE

Site:
Giza, northern Egypt

2. Use a marker and a ruler to draw stones on the triangles for the pyramid's walls.

3. Tape one side of each triangle (stone-side down) to a side of the square.

4. Bring the points of the triangle together and tape to hold.

FOLD TRIANGLES UP TOWARD CENTER

AROUND the WORLD FUN!

⚙ **King for a Day!** More than 3,000 years ago, *Tutankhamen* (too-tahn-KAH-mehn) became the king of Egypt when he was about 10 years old! Make yourself a crown with triangle shapes on a headband. If you were king, what rules would you make?

⚙ **Shapes!** Look around the room for things that are shaped like squares and triangles. How many can you see?

⚙ **Learn More!** To find out more about ancient Egypt and the pyramids, read the book *Mummies Made in Egypt* by Aliki.

Striped Zebra

Selam!

Here's a riddle: What's black and white and "read" all over? Answer: a newspaper. A zebra is also black and white. If you look at a herd of zebras you can't tell them apart. Yet, no two zebras are alike when it comes to their stripes.

Your Friend

What you do:

1. Cut two slits along the bottom of one envelope. Cut a slit in both upper corners. Lick the flap closed.

2. Cut out the zebra's head and neck, legs, and tail from the second envelope.

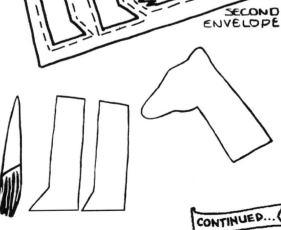

SECOND ENVELOPE

What you need:

- 2 large white envelopes
- Child safety scissors
- Black construction paper
- Glue stick
- Black marker

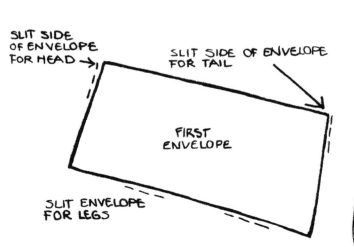

SLIT SIDE OF ENVELOPE FOR HEAD →

SLIT SIDE OF ENVELOPE FOR TAIL

FIRST ENVELOPE

SLIT ENVELOPE FOR LEGS

CONTINUED...

3. Tear thin strips of black paper and glue them diagonally across the envelope. Trim off any extra. Use a black marker to draw stripes on the zebra's head and neck, legs, and tail.

4. Glue the legs, tail, and head inside the slits in the envelope. Glue the openings closed.

TORN BLACK STRIPS

WHITE ENVELOPE

Site:
Arid, sparsely wooded areas in parts of Kenya, Ethiopia, and Somalia

AROUND the WORLD FUN!

⚙ **One of a Kind!** Pour a small amount of tempera paint onto a pad of moistened paper towels to make an ink pad. Press your fingertip into the pad and then onto paper. Compare your fingerprint with the fingerprints of your friends and family. Is each person's fingerprint different or the same?

⚙ **Learn More!** To discover more about zebras, read *The Zebra: Striped Horse* by Christine Denis-Huot.

Masai Beaded Necklace

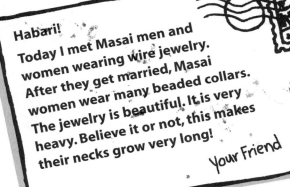

Habari!
Today I met Masai men and women wearing wire jewelry. After they get married, Masai women wear many beaded collars. The jewelry is beautiful. It is very heavy. Believe it or not, this makes their necks grow very long!

Your Friend

What you need:

- Large paper plate
- Child safety scissors
- Assorted tempera paints, in dishes or lids
- Paintbrush

CUT CENTER OUT OF LARGE PAPER PLATE

CUT CENTER

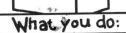

What you do:

1. Cut into the plate and then cut out the center, leaving a wide rim all around.

2. Dip the rounded end of the paintbrush handle into a color. Press dots of color around the rim of the plate. Wash off the end of the paintbrush. Then, use another color for more dots.

CONTINUED...

AROUND the WORLD FUN!

⚙ **Beads Galore!** Purchase colorful beads and thin wires from a craft store. Thread the beads onto the wires for different bracelets and necklaces.

⚙ **Learn More!** Read the book *Growing Up Masai* by Tom Shactman to learn what life is like for Masai children.

Site:
North central Tanzania, southern Kenya

Nile Crocodile

What you need:

- Brown construction paper
- Pencil
- Child safety scissors
- Sponge (small piece)
- Green tempera paint, in a dish or lid
- Black marker

What you do:

1. Fold the paper in half the long way. With the fold at the top, draw a crocodile on the paper (see art on page 70 to trace).

2. Cut out the crocodile. (Make sure you do not cut the fold along the crocodile's back, though!)

DON'T CUT ON CROCODILE'S BACK

Hello!

Today I saw a big crocodile lying in the sun! It had its mouth open wide. When it closed its mouth, two of its lower teeth stuck out. The skin on the crocodile looks just like armor.

Your Friend

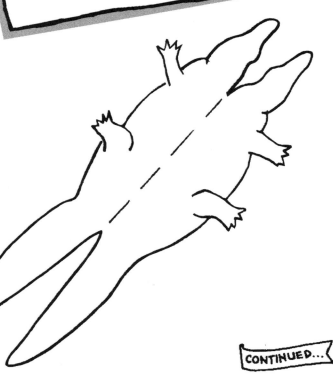

CONTINUED...

3. Dab the sponge in the paint. Press it onto the crocodile for skin. Use a marker to draw eyes and a mouth.

⚙ **Make a Crocodile Hand Puppet.** Put your hand inside an athletic sock. Push the toe of the sock into the curve of your hand between your thumb and pointer finger. Use fabric paint or a marker to draw on the crocodile's eyes. Now, move your fingers to open and close the crocodile's mouth!

⚙ **Crocodile Crafts!** To make more animal crafts, read *The Kids' Wildlife Book: Exploring Animal Worlds through Indoor/ Outdoor Crafts & Experiences* by Warner Shedd.

Site:
Found throughout tropical and southern Africa and Madagascar, in rivers, freshwater marshes, estuaries, and mangrove swamps

YOU CAN TRACE THIS ONTO YOUR FOLDED PAPER IN STEP 1.

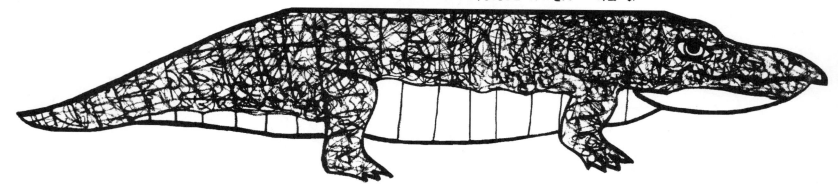

Lion Mask

What you need:

- Brown paper lunch bag
- Child safety scissors
- Pencil
- Large paper plate
- Glue stick
- Brown and black markers
- Yarn

What you do:

1. Cut open the paper bag and lay it flat. Ask a grown-up to help you trace the paper plate onto the bag. Cut out the circle slightly larger than the drawing.

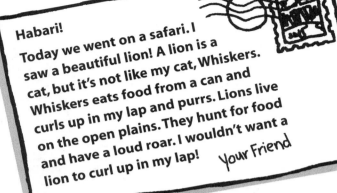

Habari!

Today we went on a safari. I saw a beautiful lion! A lion is a cat, but it's not like my cat, Whiskers. Whiskers eats food from a can and curls up in my lap and purrs. Lions live on the open plains. They hunt for food and have a loud roar. I wouldn't want a lion to curl up in my lap!

Your Friend

CONTINUED...

2. Glue the circle onto the paper plate.

3. Cut out the lion's eyes. Cut along three sides of the nose as shown. Cut fringe around the lion's face for its mane.

4. Use a pencil to poke a hole in the sides of the plate. String yarn through the holes. Use the markers to decorate the face. Put on your mask and *r-o-a-r!*

CUT ALONG THREE SIDES
OF NOSE

Site:
**Found mainly
in parts of
Africa south
of the Sahara**

⚙ **A Proud Pride.**
Lions are the most social members of the cat family. They live in a group called a *pride*. Make several paper-plate lions to make a pride of lions.

⚙ **Learn More!** Read the book *Young Lions* by Toshi Yoshida to learn how lions in Africa hunt for food.

Zulu Beehive Hut

What you need:

- Brown paper lunch bag
- Child safety scissors
- Transparent tape
- Brown marker

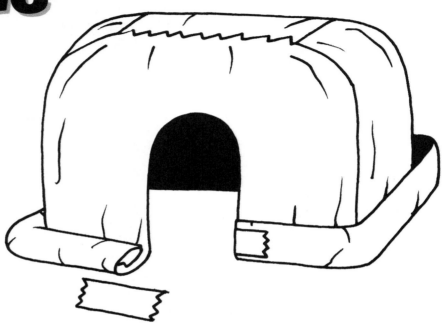

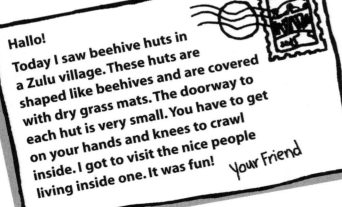

Hallo!

Today I saw beehive huts in a Zulu village. These huts are shaped like beehives and are covered with dry grass mats. The doorway to each hut is very small. You have to get on your hands and knees to crawl inside. I got to visit the nice people living inside one. It was fun!

Your Friend

What you do:

1. Cut away the top half of the bag. Hold the bottom of the bag upside down and cut out a doorway for a hut.

2. Fold up the edge of the bag for a cuff around the bottom of the hut. Tape at the corners as shown.

3. Use a marker to draw the grass mats on the hut. Push in the corners of the bag to round off the top of the hut.

CONTINUED...

Site:
**Kwazulu Natal,
southern Africa**

AROUND the WORLD FUN!

⚙ **Houses, Huts, and Hives.** Beehive huts are shaped like a beehive. They have a dome-shaped roof. Take a walk and look at the roofs on the buildings where you live. Describe the roofs that you see. Draw a picture of some of the roof shapes.

⚙ **Not a Drop!** Zulu huts in Africa are so well built out of grasses that when it rains, everyone inside stays dry. How do you stay dry on a rainy day?

Desert Sand Dune

What you need:

- Chalk, 3 or 4 colors
- Cheese grater
- Waxed paper
- Salt
- Small jar with a tight-fitting lid
- Thin paintbrush

What you do:

1. Grate each color of chalk over a sheet of waxed paper. Mix salt into the chalk.

2. Pour a layer of colored salt into the jar. Continue to add layers of different colors of salt. Fill the jar to the top.

Good morning!

I played in the sand today, but I wasn't at the beach. We were in the sand dunes in the desert. Sand dunes are always moving and changing. Wind blows grains of sand up and over the tops of the dunes and down the other side. Sand got in my shoes when I walked!

Your Friend

CONTINUED...

POKE END OF PAINT-
BRUSH INTO SALT
ALONG JAR TO
MAKE DESIGN

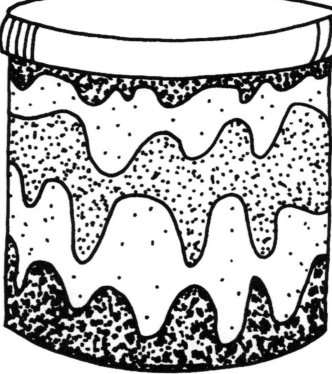

Site:
**Located in Africa
near the equator.
Other continents —
North America and
Asia, for instance —
have deserts, too.
Beach dunes can
be seen along many
coastal areas on
many continents.**

3. Poke the end of the
paintbrush into the salt along
the sides of the jar to make a
design. Tightly screw the lid
back onto the jar.

AROUND the WORLD FUN!

✪ **Paint with Sand.** Squeeze a design of white craft glue onto paper. Sprinkle different
colors of salt sand over the glue. Shake off the excess sand for a sand painting!

✪ **Beach in a Bag.** Each time you visit a beach, collect a small sandwich bag of sand. When
you get home, label the bag with the name of the beach and the date of your visit. How
does the sand from one beach compare with the sand from another beach?

Ashanti Kente Cloth

What you need:

- Assorted construction paper (3 sheets the same size, plus black)
- Child safety scissors
- Transparent tape

Greetings!

Today I saw some bright and colorful cloth, woven by Ashanti weavers. Strips of the cloth are sewn together. These kente cloths are worn during very special occasions — just like when I wear my best clothes.

Your Friend

What you do:

1. Fold the black paper in half. Starting at the fold, cut zigzag slits across the paper, stopping about 1" (2.5 cm) from the edge. Lay the paper flat.

FOLD OVER

CONTINUED...

2. Cut assorted colors of paper into strips. Weave strips of paper in and out of the slits — first *over* one slit, then *under* the next slit, through to the other side. Tape the ends of the strips to keep them in place.

3. Weave the next strip, starting *under* the slit, then going *over*. Alternate each strip until the black paper is completely woven.

TAPE THE ENDS TO KEEP IN PLACE.

TAPE →

Site:
Made in parts of Ghana and Cote d'Ivoire

AROUND the WORLD FUN!

⚙ **Weaving Leaves.** Pull out several threads from a piece of burlap fabric. Weave a collection of dried leaves, weeds, and twigs through the openings in the fabric. Hang the burlap from yarn tied to a stick.

⚙ **Coats of Many Colors.** Think about the clothes you wear on special occasions, like family dinners, birthday parties, and playtime. Think about the kinds of clothes you wear at different times of the year. How are winter and summer clothes different? How do you think African clothes might differ from your clothes?

Europe

Europe is one of the world's smaller continents. (Asia is four times as big!) And guess what? The smallest country in the world is in Europe. (It's the Vatican City.) You already may have heard of some of the countries in Europe, such as *France, England,* and *Spain.* Europe has many other countries, too, and in each one, people speak a different language. Yet, all of the people who live in Europe are called Europeans.

Even though there are many countries on this continent, the countries are all very near to one another — as near as you may be to another state or province. Imagine: Some people who live in France drive to the store in *Germany* or buy their clothes in *Switzerland!* How would you like to be able to visit another country just by hopping in your family's car and driving down the road? That would be so much fun!

Clicking Castanet

¡Hola!

We watched *flamenco* dancers click their heels very quickly on the dance floor. They danced to the music of guitars and chattering castanets. When they finished their dance, we all clapped and yelled, "Olé!"

Your Friend

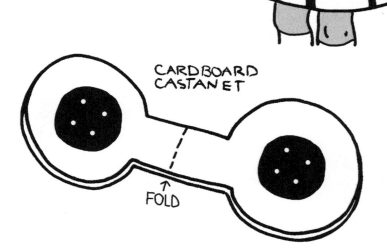

CARDBOARD CASTANET

FOLD

What you need:

- Cereal–box cardboard
- Child safety scissors
- 2 large buttons*
- Tacky glue
- Markers

Buttons pose a choking danger to young children. Adults should control the supply and insert them into the project.

What you do:

1. Cut out the shape as shown from the cardboard.

2. Glue a button on each end for castanets. Allow to dry.

3. Use markers to decorate the castanets. Fold over.

AROUND the WORLD FUN!

⚙ **Be a Spanish Dancer!** A woman flamenco dancer wears a lace *mantilla* over her head and shoulders. Ask a grown-up to help attach a scarf to your hair using barrettes. Now, hold your hands high, click your castanets and your heels, and dance!

⚙ **Play the Spoons.** Clap together two metal spoons. Hold one spoon between your thumb and index finger with the spoon facing up. Hold the second spoon, bottom facing up, between your third and fourth fingers. To play the spoons, sit down and click the spoons between your thigh and the palm of your other hand.

Site: Used specifically in Spain, but also wherever there are flamenco dancers. Variations can be found throughout Eastern Europe into Asia.

Eiffel Tower

What you need:

- Construction paper (3 sheets)
- Transparent tape
- Child safety scissors
- Pencil
- Sharp scissors (for grown-up use only)
- Black marker

What you do:

1. Fold one sheet of construction paper in half the long way. Open it, lay it flat, and fold each long side to the center crease. Tape the long sides together to make a long rectangular tube.

Bonjour!

I took an elevator to the top of the Eiffel Tower this evening. When I got to the top I looked out over the city. I could see all of Paris. What a beautiful sight! Now I know why it's called the "City of Lights!"

Your Friend

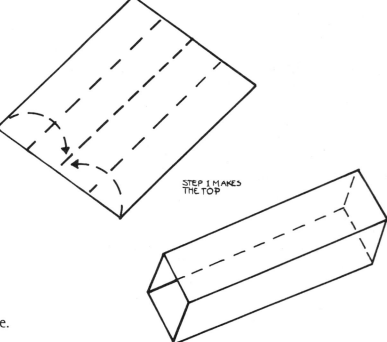

STEP 1 MAKES THE TOP

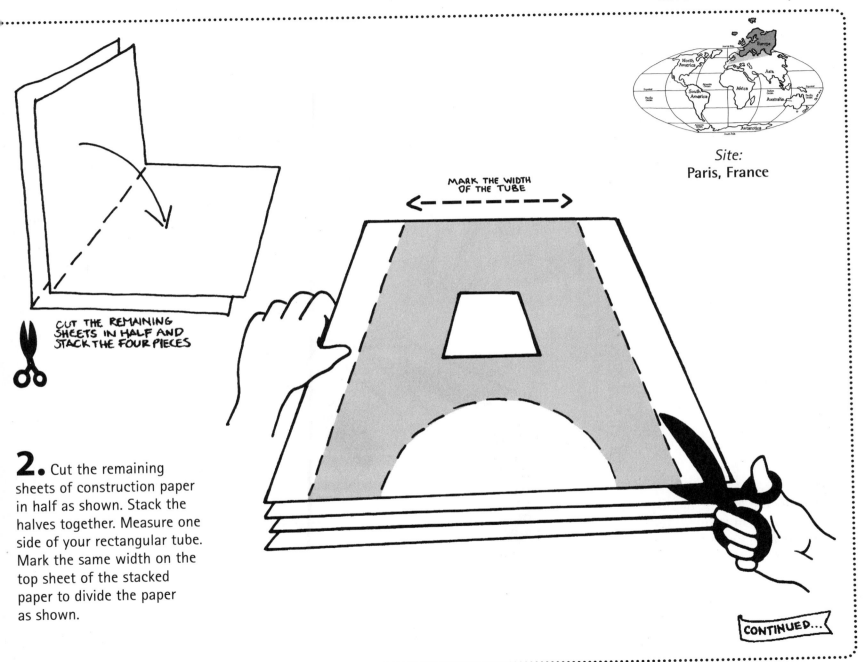

Site:
Paris, France

MARK THE WIDTH
OF THE TUBE

CUT THE REMAINING
SHEETS IN HALF AND
STACK THE FOUR PIECES

2. Cut the remaining sheets of construction paper in half as shown. Stack the halves together. Measure one side of your rectangular tube. Mark the same width on the top sheet of the stacked paper to divide the paper as shown.

CONTINUED...

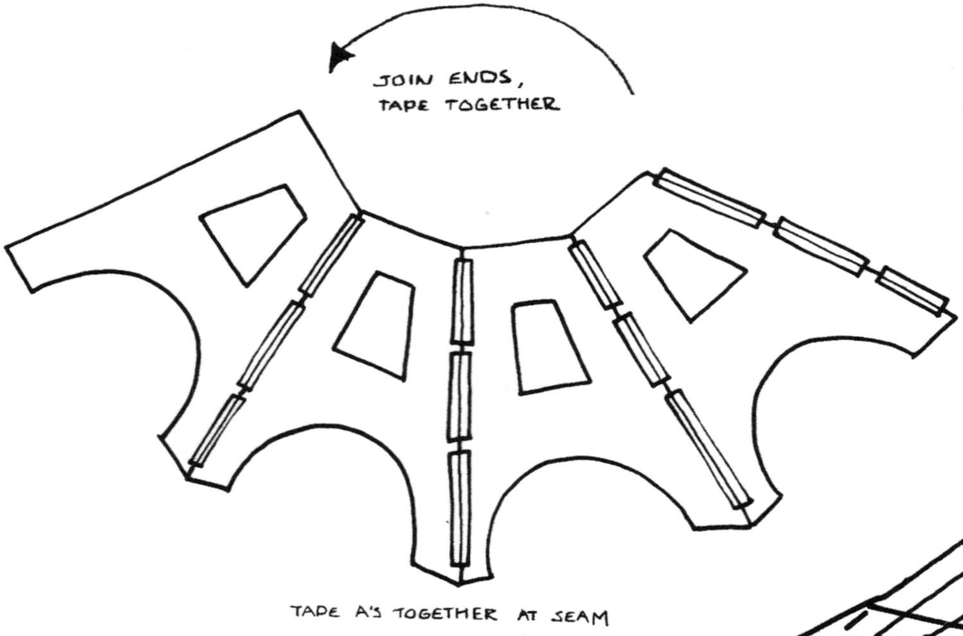

JOIN ENDS,
TAPE TOGETHER

TAPE A'S TOGETHER AT SEAM

3. Using the lines as the top of the letter A, draw the sides of the letter down the paper. Ask a grown-up to cut out the A, going through all four sheets of paper.

4. Lay the A's side by side, then tape them together for the tower's base. Insert the paper tube in the top and tape to hold.

5. Use the marker to draw supports onto the tower.

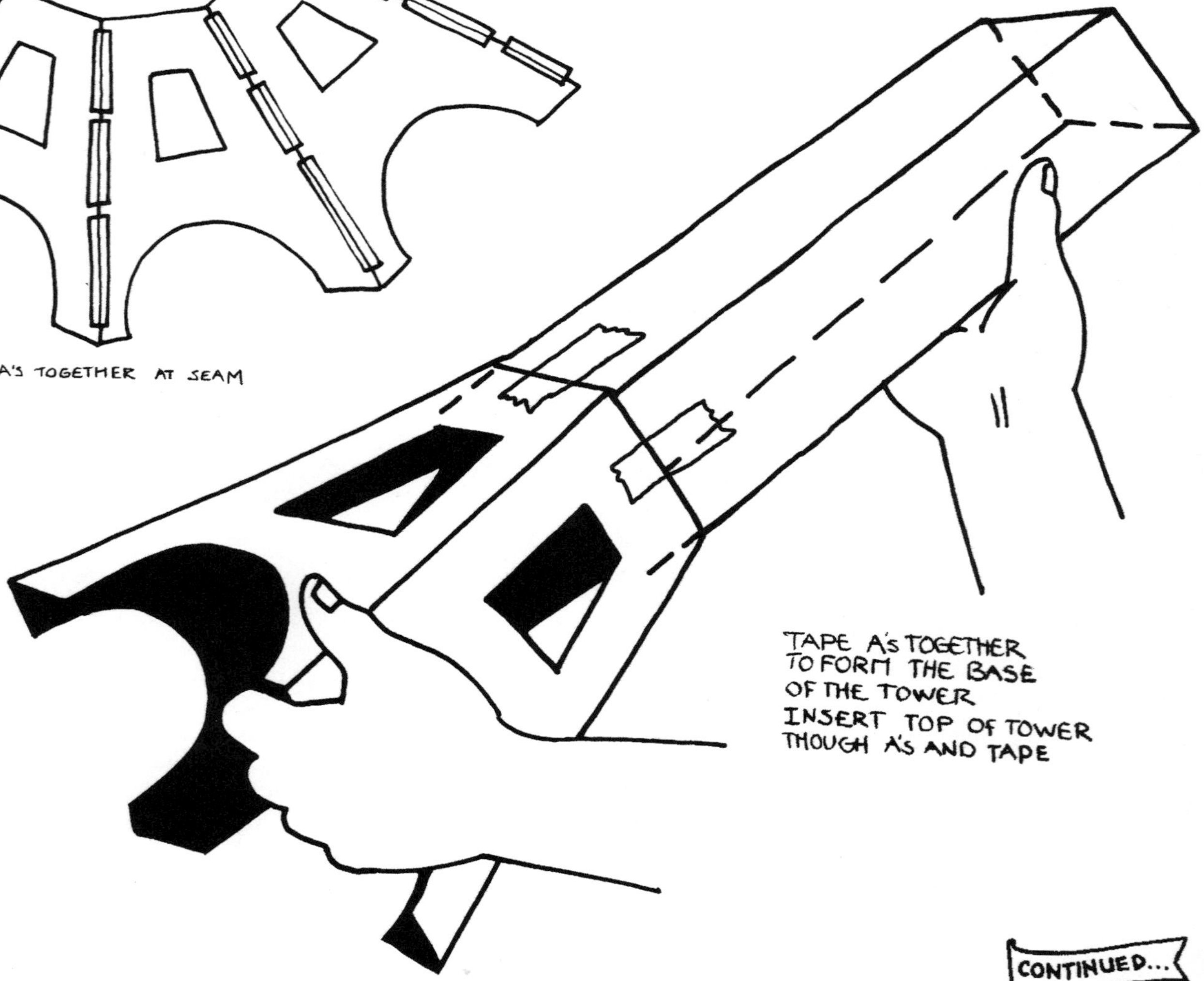

TAPE A'S TOGETHER
TO FORM THE BASE
OF THE TOWER
INSERT TOP OF TOWER
THOUGH A'S AND TAPE

CONTINUED...

AROUND the WORLD FUN!

⚙ **The Nose Knows.**
Locally grown flowers such as wild lavender, jasmine, and violets are used to create French perfumes. Smell the flowers that grow where you live. Ask a florist or gardener if you could have some flowers that have gone by. Place the petals in a bowl. Do they make your room smell nice?

⚙ **Story Corner.**
Read the timeless and enchanting *The Adventures of Jeanne-Marie* by Françoise.

Decorated Egg

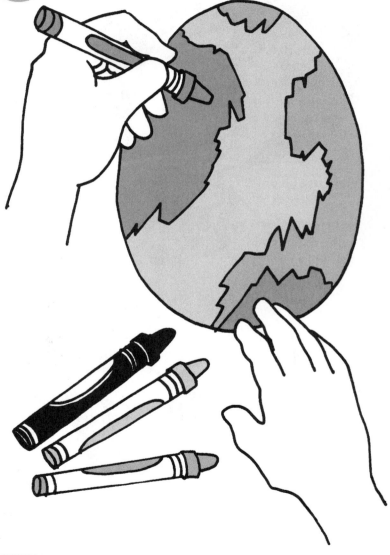

Nazdar!

In the marketplace this morning I saw beautifully decorated eggs. These eggs are called *pysanky*. Each egg has a different design. The designs are made with wax and dye. They're too beautiful to eat!

Your Friend

What you need:

- Small white paper plate
- Child safety scissors
- Crayons (including black)
- Pencil with a dull point or toothpicks

What you do:

1. Cut out the shape of an egg from the center of the paper plate.

2. Use colorful crayons to cover the egg with blotches of color.

3. Color heavily over the whole egg with a black crayon.

4. Use the pencil to scratch designs in the egg.

Site:
A popular craft in Eastern Europe and many parts of Russia

AROUND the WORLD FUN!

☼ **Eggs-traordinary!** Very gently draw designs on the shell of a raw egg using a white crayon or a wax candle Hold the egg over a bowl. Ask a grown-up to poke a very small hole in each end. Use a straw to blow the contents of the egg into the bowl.* Carefully wash the egg in soap and water. Dip it into a cup of water mixed with a few drops of food coloring. Remove the egg and let it dry. The food coloring won't stick to the wax design, so you'll have a pysanky-style egg!

☼ **Egyptian Egg Art.** Lots of countries make colored eggs to celebrate the spring. Ask a grown-up to help you cut out an egg shape from cardboard. Fill a cup with water and a few drops of food coloring. Break eggshells into small pieces* and place them in the food coloring. Strain the shells when colored and pat them dry with paper towels. Cover the cardboard with glue and press on the colored eggshell pieces.

*Save the eggs' insides to make breakfast!

Matryoshka

What you need:

- Assorted construction paper
- Child safety scissors
- Transparent tape
- Markers

Strozveetsya!

Big, bigger, biggest. These nesting dolls fit inside each other! Just when you think you've uncovered the smallest doll, there's one that's even smaller. When they're standing in a row, they look like a doll family!

Your Friend

What you do:

1. Cut out half circles, going from large to small, from different colors of construction paper. Bend in and tape the corners together.

2. Cut out faces from construction paper, going from large to small. Use markers to draw eyes, nose, mouth, and hair on each face.

3. Tape the faces inside the taped half circles. Stack the dolls, starting with the smallest and ending with the largest.

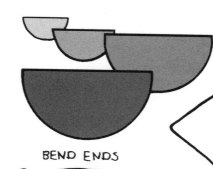

BEND ENDS

TAPE

TAPE ENDS TOGETHER

Site:
Most popular in Russia, though they can be found in Eastern Europe as well

AROUND the WORLD FUN!

- ⚙ **Around-the-World Names.** *Matryoshka* means "a little Matryona." *Matryona* is the Russian word for "mother." Do you have a nickname? Ask your friends and family what they like to be called.

- ⚙ **Size Things Up.** Arrange things like cans, boxes, toy cars, or stuffed animals according to size. Start with the biggest and move to the smallest. Then, reverse the order.

Castle

Guten tag!
We saw many castles when we went for a boat ride down the Rhine River yesterday. Castles were built as forts so that the owners could protect their lands and their families. Imagine living in a house that big!

Your Friend

What you need:

- Cereal-box cardboard
- Sharp scissors (for grown-up use only)
- Construction paper (one color plus black and a scrap of red)
- Transparent tape
- 2 cardboard toilet-paper tubes
- Tacky glue
- Child safety scissors
- Black marker

What you do:

1. Ask a grown-up to cut the cereal box in half. Wrap the top half of the box in construction paper and tape to hold.

2. Wrap the cardboard tubes in construction paper. Glue a tube to each side of the cereal box.

3. Cut out a 6" (15 cm) circle from the black paper. Make a single cut from the outside edge of the circle into the center. Overlap the edges and tape them together to form a peaked turret. Glue a roof on top of each tube.

4. Use the marker to draw stones, windows, and a doorway on the castle. Cut two flags from the red paper and glue one onto each turret.

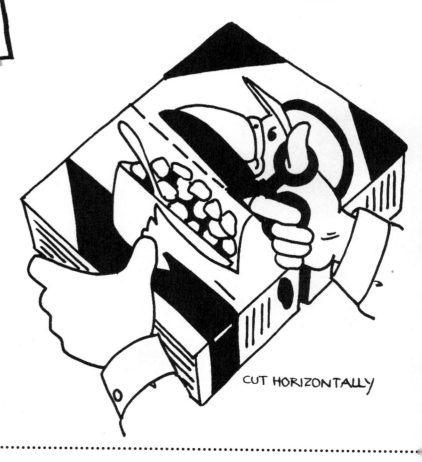

CUT HORIZONTALLY

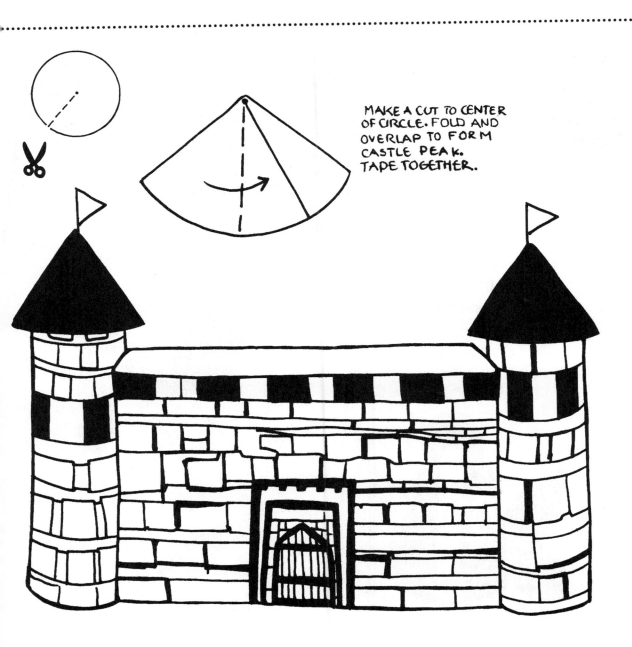

MAKE A CUT TO CENTER OF CIRCLE. FOLD AND OVERLAP TO FORM CASTLE PEAK. TAPE TOGETHER.

Site:
Found throughout Europe, with many of the best-preserved examples in Germany

⚙ **Build a Castle.** Use things found in your kitchen cupboard. How about tin cans for towers and cardboard boxes for walls? What will you put inside your castle? How about small dolls, action figures, and animals?

⚙ **Story Corner.** Look at the book *Into the Castle* by June Crebbin.

The Little Mermaid

What you need:

- Old magazine or photo
- Child safety scissors
- Green construction paper
- Glue stick
- Popsicle stick
- Paper cup

Davs!

This afternoon I saw the Little Mermaid, a statue that sits in the harbor in Copenhagen. She's supposed to be half-human and half-fish. This mermaid is sitting on a rock looking out to sea. I wonder what she is thinking about.

Your Friend

What you do:

1. Cut out a picture of a person from an old magazine or photo (maybe one of you!). Cut away the legs in the picture.

2. Cut out fins from the green construction paper. Glue the fins onto the picture to make a mermaid.

3. Glue the mermaid onto the Popsicle stick. Cut a slit in the bottom of the cup, then push the Popsicle stick down into the slit.

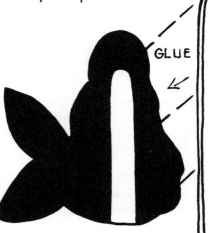

GLUE

GLUE BACK OF MERMAID TO POPSICLE STICK

CUT A SLIT IN BOTTOM OF CUP FOR STICK

Site:
**Statue of the Little
Mermaid from the fairy tale
by Hans Christian Andersen
in Copenhagen, Denmark**

⚙ **Mythical Animal Match.** Draw or paint pictures of pretend animals like unicorns, mermaids, and dragons onto index cards. Cut the index cards in half. Turn the cards face-down. The first player turns two cards over. If the halves match, that player keeps the cards. If not, the player turns the cards back over and it's the next player's turn. Take turns until there are no cards left.

⚙ **Story Corner.** Read the book *The Mermaid Lullaby* by Kate Spohn.

Windmill

What you need:

> **Dag!**
> Today we walked through a park where there were millions of tulips. I liked the red ones best. Tomorrow we'll see lots of windmills. I hope it's a windy day and they spin very fast!
>
> Your Friend

- Round cardboard carton with lid (oatmeal, cornmeal, or bread-crumb container)
- Assorted construction paper
- Transparent tape
- Child safety scissors
- Black marker
- Sharp pointed tool (for grown-up use only)
- Paper fastener*

Paper fasteners pose a choking and poking danger to young children. Adults should control the supply and help insert them into the project.

AROUND the WORLD FUN!

⬭ **Tide's In!** In Holland, the land is very low, and the sea is very high. *Dikes* are strong walls that hold back the sea. If you go to the beach, build a sand dike (wall) close to the shoreline. What happens to your dike when the tide comes in?

⬭ **Bulb Magic.** Tulips grow all over Holland. These flowers grow from *bulbs*. Did you know that we eat some bulbs, such as onions, and garlic? Put an onion in a brown bag. Wait a week or two, then look inside to see what is growing. Surprise?

⬭ **Story Corner.** Read the book *The Hole in the Dike* retold by Norma Green and illustrated by Eric Carle.

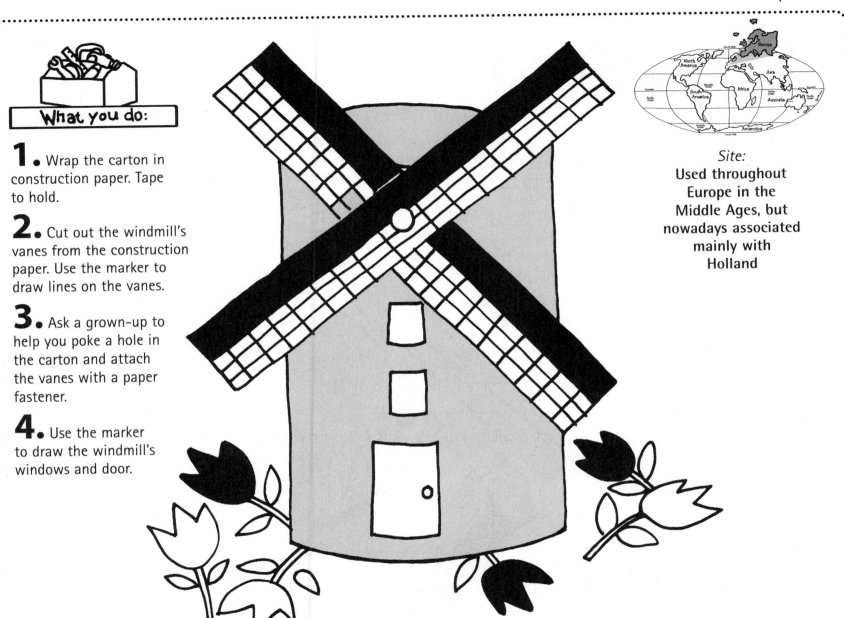

What you do:

1. Wrap the carton in construction paper. Tape to hold.

2. Cut out the windmill's vanes from the construction paper. Use the marker to draw lines on the vanes.

3. Ask a grown-up to help you poke a hole in the carton and attach the vanes with a paper fastener.

4. Use the marker to draw the windmill's windows and door.

Site:
Used throughout Europe in the Middle Ages, but nowadays associated mainly with Holland

Royal Crown

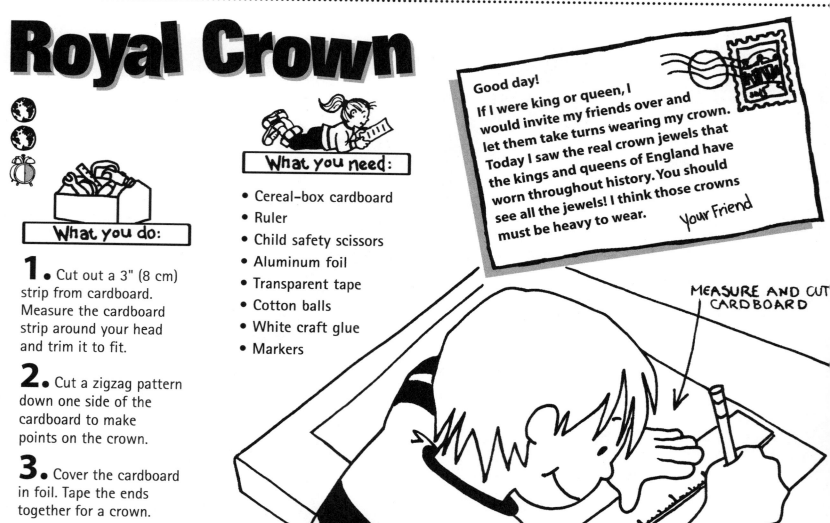

What you do:

1. Cut out a 3" (8 cm) strip from cardboard. Measure the cardboard strip around your head and trim it to fit.

2. Cut a zigzag pattern down one side of the cardboard to make points on the crown.

3. Cover the cardboard in foil. Tape the ends together for a crown.

4. Glue cotton balls around the base of the crown. Use markers to decorate the crown. Let dry.

What you need:

- Cereal-box cardboard
- Ruler
- Child safety scissors
- Aluminum foil
- Transparent tape
- Cotton balls
- White craft glue
- Markers

Good day!

If I were king or queen, I would invite my friends over and let them take turns wearing my crown. Today I saw the real crown jewels that the kings and queens of England have worn throughout history. You should see all the jewels! I think those crowns must be heavy to wear.

Your Friend

MEASURE AND CUT CARDBOARD

"Crackers"! No, these aren't the kind you eat with peanut butter. These are English party favors. To make a cracker, fill a cardboard toilet-paper tube with sweets and small toys. Wrap the tube in gift-wrap paper that's twice as long as the tube. Twist the ends of the paper and tie them with ribbon or yarn. Then, have a royal English party and wear your crown!

A Royal Website!
To see photos of the real crown jewels of England, check out this website: **www.camelot-group.com/tower_site/jewels/index.html**

Site:
British crown jewels on display in the Tower of London, London, England

Loch Ness Monster

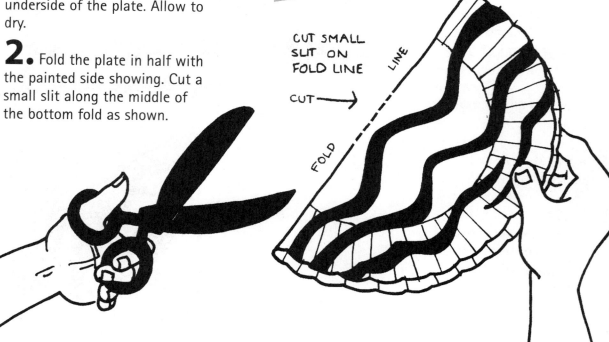

Ciamar a tha thu?

Legend has it that there's a shy monster called "Nessie" living in the Loch Ness. We went for a boat ride on the lake. I looked for the monster but didn't see it.

Your Friend

What you do:

1. Use the paints to color the underside of the plate. Allow to dry.

2. Fold the plate in half with the painted side showing. Cut a small slit along the middle of the bottom fold as shown.

CUT SMALL SLIT ON FOLD LINE

LINE

CUT →

FOLD

What you need:

- Blue and green watercolor paints
- Paintbrush
- Small white paper plate
- Child safety scissors
- Green construction paper
- Black marker
- Popsicle stick
- Glue stick

3. Cut out the Loch Ness monster from the green paper. Use the marker to draw on the monster's face. Glue the monster onto the stick.

4. Insert the stick through the slit in the plate. Glue the corners of the plate together. Now, move the stick to move the monster!

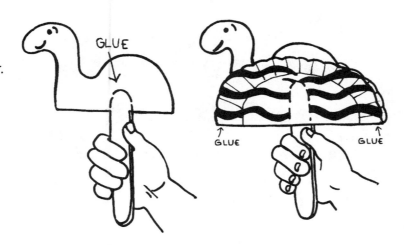

GLUE

GLUE   GLUE

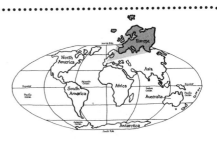

Site:
Loch Ness, Scotland

AROUND the WORLD FUN!

⚙ **Family Fabrics.** In the Scottish highlands, people wear special plaid clothing with a certain pattern and color that is their "family" cloth. Use markers to make up a plaid pattern on paper for your family.

⚙ **Monster Madness!** Everyone loves Nessie. Did you know she even has a fan club? Visit the club's website at: **www. lochness.co.uk/fan_ club/index.html**

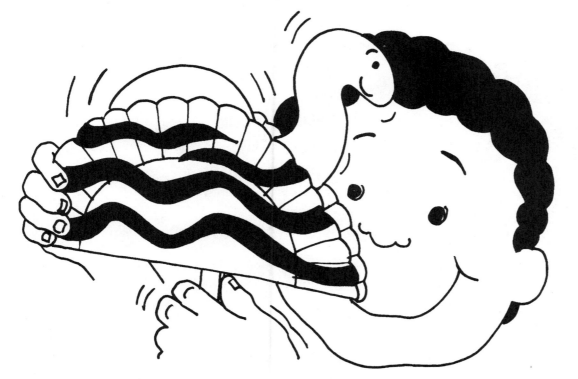

This continent was named for the European explorer *Amerigo Vespucci* — just like North America was. Actually, the name "America" first meant only South America. Later, all three areas became known as the Americas.

Except for Antarctica, South America goes farther south than any other continent. And like Antarctica, it has some very cold spots, especially the Andes Mountains, which run almost all the way up the western side of the continent.

Other parts of this continent have beautiful rain forests with wonderful animals and plants that you can see only there. It will be so much fun to walk through a rain forest, seeing all of the strange, colorful birds and listening to the unusual sounds they make! I'd better bring an umbrella in case it starts to rain!

Central and South America

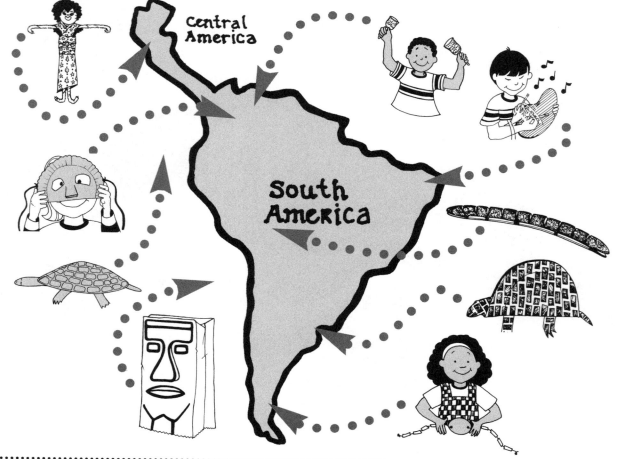

Central America

South America

Worry Doll

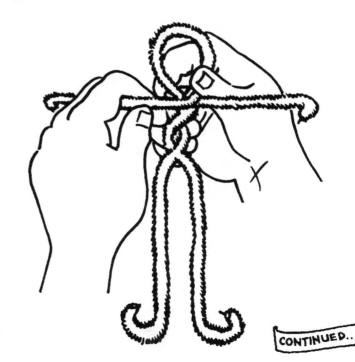

¡Hola!
Tonight I'll put a worry doll under my pillow just like the kids in Central America do. Before I fall asleep, I can tell it all my worries. In the morning when I wake up, my worries will be gone! That's what the tradition of the worry doll says.

Your Friend

What you need:

- 1 ½ pipe cleaners
- Child safety scissors
- Scrap construction paper
- Markers
- Tacky glue
- Yarn
- Scrap fabric (small pieces)

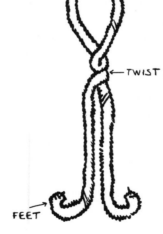

LOOP

← TWIST

FEET

What you do:

1. Bend the whole pipe cleaner in half so a loop forms in the top. Twist the loop to make the doll's head. Bend the ends of the cleaner for the doll's feet.

2. Wrap the half-cleaner around the bottom of the loop for arms.

CONTINUED...

3. Cut out the doll's face from scrap paper. Use markers to draw on the doll's eyes, nose, mouth, and ears. Glue the face onto the loop. Glue on yarn for hair.

4. Wrap scrap fabric around the doll and glue to hold.

WRAP DOLL IN MATERIAL AND GLUE

Site:
Guatemala and parts of Mexico

AROUND the WORLD FUN!

⚙ **Make a Doll Family.** Dolls of all different sizes can be found in the open-air markets of Central America. Try making a smaller worry doll. How small a piece of pipe cleaner will you need? Have fun making a whole family of dolls — and make some to give to friends, too.

⚙ **Bejeweled!** Attach a small pipe cleaner loop around a small worry doll and through a ponytail holder, safety pin, or barrette for a great piece of craft jewelry.

Musical Maraca

What you need:

- Yogurt cup
- Seeds or beans
- Clear plastic wrap
- Rubber band
- Child safety scissors
- Brown paper lunch bag
- Transparent tape
- Markers

¡Hola!

I like the rattling sound of the shaking maraca. Maracas used to be made from dried gourd shells that had seeds inside. The maraca I played was made from wood. It was fun to hold a maraca in each hand and play along with songs I heard!

Your Friend

WRAP CUP IN PAPER BAG
TAPE TO HOLD

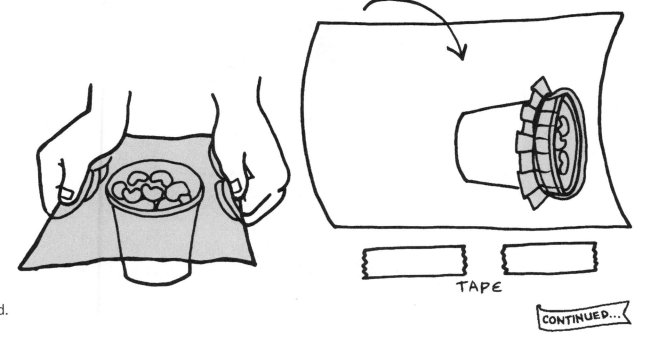

TAPE

What you do:

1. Fill the empty cup with dried beans or seeds. Cover the opening with plastic wrap and secure with the rubber band.

2. Cut open the paper bag and lay it flat. Wrap the cup inside. Tape to hold.

CONTINUED...

Site:
Gourd maracas are very common in Venezuela, although variations of this instrument can be found all over the world.

3. Twist the excess bag to form a handle. Wrap tape around the handle. Now, decorate your maraca with markers and give it a shake!

AROUND the WORLD FUN!

⚙ **Maraca Madness!** Gather some maracas, a block of wood and a spoon, and a spoon and a pot lid. Have a parade. Put on some music and march around!

⚙ **Learn More!** To find out more about other percussion instruments from around the world, read *Bang and Rattle* by Ruth Thomson and Sally Hewitt or *Wood-Hoopoe Willie* by Katherine Roundtree and Virginia L. Kroll.

Gold Mask

What you need:

- Large paper plate
- Child safety scissors
- Pencil
- Yarn
- Aluminum foil
- Glue stick
- Yellow or orange marker

What you do:

1. Cut away the bottom third of the paper plate. On the remaining piece, draw eyes and a nose. Cut out the eyes. Cut along three sides of the nose as shown.

¡Hola!

I'm visiting ancient ruins and guess what I saw — gold! The early people of Colombia mined gold from rivers and mountains. They believed that gold was the "sweat of the sun." They made golden masks, statues, animal figures, drinking cups, and even a tiny gold raft. Just imagine how beautiful they all are!

Your Friend

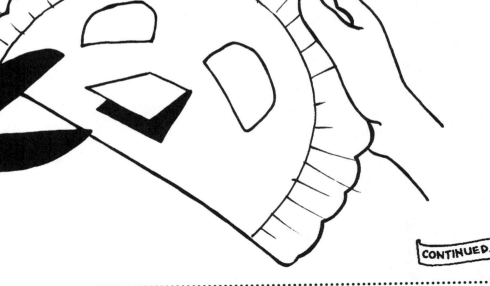

CONTINUED...

2. Use a pencil to poke a hole on opposite sides of the plate. Thread yarn through each hole.

3. Glue pieces of aluminum foil onto the plate until the mask is covered. Use a marker to color it "gold." Let dry.

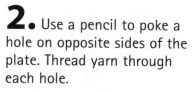

Site:
Found in The Gold Museum in Santafé de Bogotá, Colombia, although gold masks were also cast in ancient Egypt

GLUE ON FOIL AND THEN COLOR WITH MARKER

AROUND the WORLD FUN!

⚙ **Have a Treasure Hunt.** Gather several small rocks. Paint them gold. Hide the rocks around your house or yard. At the word "Go," players hunt for the rocks.

⚙ **Celebrate!** Just think how much fun it would be to wear your mask in an Indian or Spanish carnival or parade. To find out about celebrations, read *Hands Around the World* by Susan Milord.

Giant Tortoise

What you need:

- Brown paper grocery bag
- Child safety scissors
- Transparent tape
- Brown marker

What you do:

1. Cut open the bag so it lays flat. Cut out a large oval from the bag.

2. Cut a slit in both ends of the oval. Overlap the ends of each slit and tape each to hold for the tortoise's curved shell.

¡Hola!

I saw a giant tortoise, and it sure moved slowly. It has to go slowly because it's so big and weighs so much. The tortoise we saw weighed as much as two baby elephants! I wonder how he can swim!

Your Friend

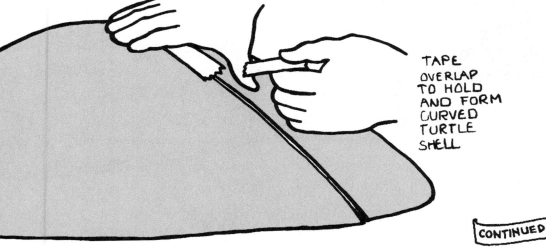

TAPE
OVERLAP
TO HOLD
AND FORM
CURVED
TURTLE
SHELL

CONTINUED...

3. Cut out the tortoise's head, tail, and feet from the rest of the bag. Tape to the underside of the shell. Use the marker to draw a pattern onto the tortoise's shell.

⚙ **Story Corner.** Read the wonderful tale of *The Foolish Tortoise* by Richard Buckley.

⚙ **Learn More!** Giant tortoises are *endangered* animals. That means we need to make sure their babies, called *tortoise hatchlings*, are able to grow up. Read the book *Gone Forever!* by Sandra and William Markele to learn more about endangered animals.

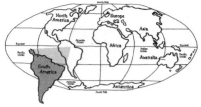

Site:
**Most islands
in the Galápagos Islands
in the east Pacific
off the coast
of Ecuador**

Emerald Tree Boa Constrictor

- Green construction paper
- Transparent tape
- Child safety scissors
- Sponge (small piece)
- White tempera paint, in a dish or lid
- Black marker

¡Hola!

Walking through a jungle, I saw a bright green boa constrictor in a tree above me. It stayed in the tree by wrapping itself around a thick branch. Up in the trees it finds monkeys and birds to eat. I'm glad I'm on the ground!

Your Friend

What you do:

1. Roll the green paper into a long, thin tube. Tape to hold.

2. Cut around the ends of the tube for the snake's tail and head.

ROLL GREEN PAPER INTO TUBE. TAPE TO HOLD

CUT AROUND ENDS TO FORM TAIL AND HEAD

CONTINUED...

3. Starting below the head, cut slits about 1" (2.5 cm) apart, being careful not to cut all the way through the tube.

4. Dab the sponge into the paint. Press it onto the tube for the snake's skin. Use the marker to draw the snake's eyes and mouth.

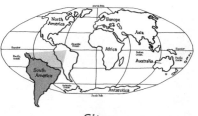

Site:
tropical South America

CUT 1" SLITS BELOW HEAD.
BE CAREFUL NOT TO CUT
THROUGH TUBE.

AROUND the WORLD FUN!

☼ **Hometown Habitat.** Do you see squirrels, birds, or rabbits where you live? Draw a picture of the wildlife near your home.

☼ **Take a "Smell Test"!** A snake smells with its tongue, as well as its nose. Try taking a "smell test." Gather things that have strong smells, like onions, lemons, pickles, coffee, and flowers. Put on a blindfold and see how many things you can identify just by their smell.

Carved Stone Statue

¡Hola!

Today on Easter Island I saw many giant statues, but no one could tell me how they got there. Some of the statues are as tall as a three-story building! That's taller than many houses we see. None of the statues has a happy face. Who do you think might have carved them?

Your Friend

What you need:

- 2 brown paper lunch bags
- Old newspapers
- Brown marker
- Child safety scissors

What you do:

1. Loosely stuff the first bag with crumpled newspapers.

2. Hold the second bag upside down and draw on the statue's face with the brown marker.

3. Cut around three sides of the nose as shown.

CONTINUED...

4. Place the second bag over the stuffed bag for a 3-D statue.

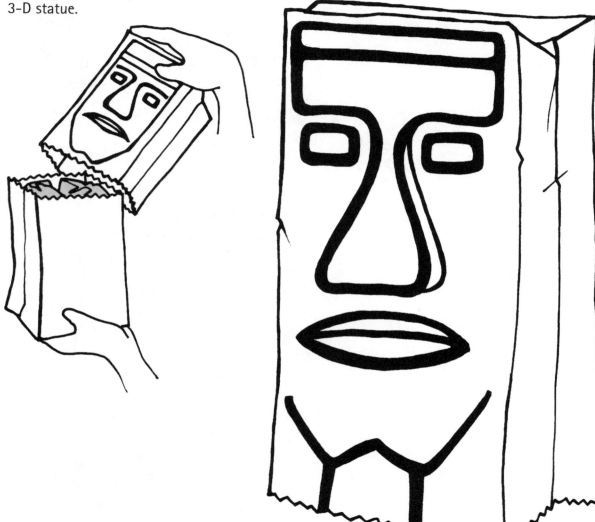

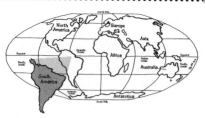

Site:
Easter Island, Chile

⚙ **Create a Story.** Imagine you came across stone statues with sad faces. What would you think those statues were sad about and why would the carvers have made them so sad? Make up a story to explain the "mystery behind the stone statues."

⚙ **Mysterious Places!**
To see photos of the real Easter Island statues, check out this website: **www.mysterious-places.com/**

Gaucho Belt

What you need:

- Cereal-box cardboard
- Child safety scissors
- Pencil
- Aluminum foil
- Transparent tape
- Yarn
- Plastic straws

What you do:

1. Cut an oval shape from the cardboard. Use a pencil to poke a hole in each end. Cover the oval with foil and tape to hold.

¡Hola!

We rode on horseback today, just like the gauchos! Gauchos rode the *pampas* (plains) on horseback, much like the cowboys of the old West did! They tamed wild horses and herded cattle. Gauchos wore thick leather belts decorated with silver and sometimes with old coins.

Your Friend

CONTINUED...

2. Measure the yarn to fit around your waist, with some extra for tying. Then, cut the whole length in half. Tie one end of each half through a hole in the oval buckle.

3. Cut the straws into 2" (5 cm) lengths. Thread the pieces onto the yarn ties. Knot the yarn after the last straw on each side. Now, put on your gaucho belt!

MEASURE YARN TO FIT AROUND YOUR WAIST AND CUT

Site: **Argentina**

AROUND the WORLD FUN!

⚙ **Jazz it Up!** Here's a way to decorate the silver buckle on your gaucho belt. Before adding the foil, glue some string in a decorative pattern onto the cardboard. Allow the glue to dry. Then, wrap the cardboard in foil. Gently press over the foil to reveal the string design.

⚙ **Story Corner.** Read *The Magic Bean Tree: A Legend from Argentina* by Nancy Van Laan.

Reco-Reco

- Corrugated cardboard
- Sharp scissors (for grown-up use only)
- Unsharpened pencil

Olá!

I played a South American instrument today. The reco-reco is a scraper type of instrument. You scrape the stick along the strings to make a great sound. It is a percussion instrument like bells, drums, cymbals, and the triangle. I'd like to take reco-reco lessons when we get home so I can play in a band.

Your Friend

What you do:

1. Ask a grown-up to help you cut out a fancy shape from the cardboard.

2. Peel back the top layer of the cardboard to reveal the ribs.

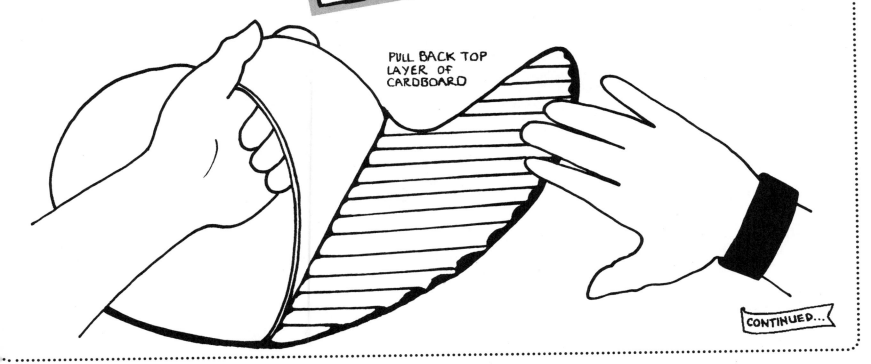

PULL BACK TOP LAYER OF CARDBOARD

CONTINUED...

3. Scrape the pencil across the ribs to create sounds.

Site:
Brazil

AROUND the WORLD FUN!

⚙ **Instruments Everywhere!** In ancient times, people made instruments out of things they found. Look for things around your house and outdoors that will make a scraping sound. Try running the pencil over the trunk of a tree, a concrete sidewalk, and a cheese grater. Listen to the different sounds they make. Which do you like the best?

⚙ **Learn More!** Brazil is home to the Amazon River, one of the greatest rivers in the world. To learn more about life in the forests of the Amazon, read *The Great Kapok Tree: A Tale of the Amazon Rain Forest* by Lynne Cherry.

Giant Armadillo

What you need:

- 2 small paper plates
- Child safety scissors
- Cereal-box cardboard
- Transparent tape
- Brown tempera paint, in a dish or lid
- Black marker

¡Hola!
I scared an armadillo today, but I didn't mean to! This funny animal carries its own armor — a shell made of strips of hard material called *scutes*. When I got close to the armadillo, it rolled up into a ball. It was protecting itself because it didn't know I was friendly.

Your Friend

What you do:

1. Cut out the armadillo's head, tail, and legs from the first paper plate.

2. Cut out a 1/2" x 2" (1 x 5 cm) strip of cardboard. Bend the cardboard into a triangle, pinch the ends together, and tape to hold for a "stamp."

1/2" (1CM)

2" (5cm)

CUT HEAD, TAIL AND LEGS FROM PAPER PLATE

PINCH

CONTINUED...

3. Dab the flat end of the stamp into the paint. Press it onto the second paper plate, and the head, tail, and legs for the armadillo's plates. Let the paint dry.

4. Fold the plate in half. Tape the armadillo's head, tail, and legs inside the plate. Tape the plate together. Use the marker to draw the eyes and mouth.

Site:
Uruguay and other parts of South and Central America and in Texas, southern Oklahoma, Louisiana, Arkansas, Mississippi, and parts of Florida

TAPE TOGETHER

AROUND the WORLD FUN!

⊗ **Animals with Armor!** Can you name other animals that have a protective outer covering like the armadillo? How about a porcupine? Now, you think of another one!

⊗ **Learn More!** To find out more about the armadillo, read *The Astonishing Armadillo* by Dee Stuart.

Antarctica

Of all the continents, Antarctica is the farthest south, which might make you think it's very hot. But not this continent! Antarctica is one of the coldest places in the world. It's actually made up of many mountain-ous islands. Guess what holds all of those islands together? A whole lot of ice! Sometimes this ice breaks off and floats out to sea. That's what makes all of the icebergs you see in pictures of Antarctica.

Believe it or not, tourists visit Antarctica, but there are no shops or schools. The only people living there are scientists who study the earth to find ways for us to take better care of it. If you ever go, better bring lots of mittens and scarves — along with your ice skates!

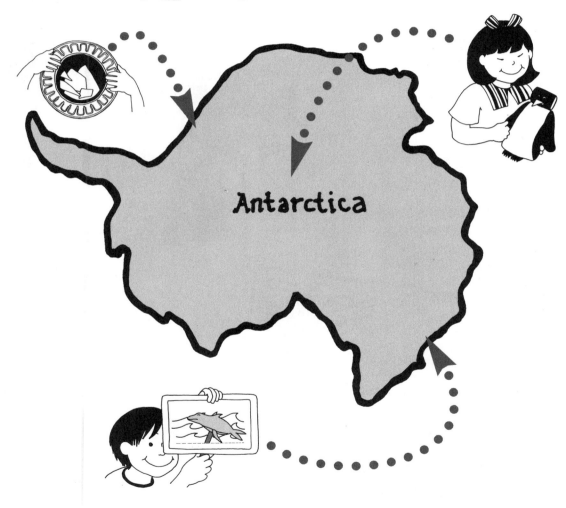

Antarctica

Adélie Penguin

What you need:

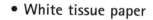

- White tissue paper
- Child safety scissors
- Cardboard toilet-paper tube
- Black tempera paint, in a dish or lid
- Paintbrush
- Construction paper (black and a scrap of orange)
- Tacky glue
- Wiggly eyes

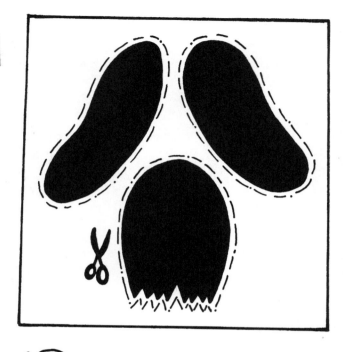

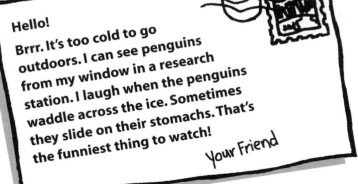

Hello!

Brrr. It's too cold to go outdoors. I can see penguins from my window in a research station. I laugh when the penguins waddle across the ice. Sometimes they slide on their stomachs. That's the funniest thing to watch!

Your Friend

What you do:

1. Cut out several layers of tissue paper longer than the cardboard tube. Wrap the tube in tissue paper and tuck in the ends.

2. Use paint to color the back of the penguin black. Let it dry.

3. Cut a strip of black paper and roll it into a tube for the penguin's head. Tape the end to secure. Glue on an orange paper beak and wiggly eyes. Then, glue the penguin's head onto the tube.

4. Cut out the wings and feet from the black paper. Glue them onto the penguin as shown.

AROUND the WORLD FUN!

⚙ **Indoor Snowflakes.** Do you know how cold it is in Antarctica? If you spilled a cup of hot water, it would turn to ice before it hit the ground! Make a snowflake that won't melt — out of paper! Trace a plate onto a sheet of white paper and cut it out. Fold the paper circle in half. Fold each corner into the center for a cone. Cut out shapes along the edges of the cone. Unfold the paper to see your snowflake.

⚙ **Funny Penguins!** Check out this website to learn more about penguins: **http://home.capu.net/~kwelch/penguins/**

Site:
Found on islands in the subantarctic and on cool coasts of Africa, Australia, New Zealand, and South America. Only the Adélie penguin and the emperor penguin reach Antarctica itself.

Icebergs

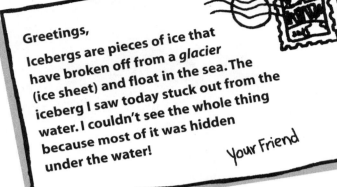

Greetings,

Icebergs are pieces of ice that have broken off from a *glacier* (ice sheet) and float in the sea. The iceberg I saw today stuck out from the water. I couldn't see the whole thing because most of it was hidden under the water!

Your Friend

What you need:

- 2 Styrofoam plates
- Child safety scissors
- Clear or blue plastic wrap
- Transparent tape
- Blue construction paper
- Tacky glue

What you do:

1. Cut out the center of one Styrofoam plate. Tape plastic wrap across the opening. Cut the center of the plate into iceberg shapes.

2. Glue blue paper onto the center of the second plate. Glue the icebergs onto the blue paper.

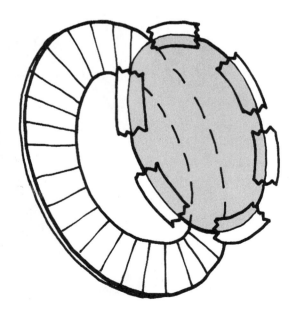

Site:
**Common in
both the
Arctic and
Antarctic regions
and are often
carried into
lower latitudes
by sea currents,
particularly
in the
North Atlantic
Ocean**

3. Place the first plate upside down on top of the second plate. Tape the plates together.

AROUND the WORLD FUN!

⚙ **Silly Science.** Pour some water into a glass and add a couple of ice cubes. Now poke them down with your finger. They pop up again! The ice is lighter than the water, so it floats. That's what keeps icebergs from sinking to the bottom of the ocean!

⚙ **Disappearing Act.** Fill a container with snow. Let the snow melt; then, look to see how much water is left. Is the water level lower than the level of the snow? Snow takes up more space because it contains a lot of air!

Blue Whale

> Greetings!
>
> Before I leave Antarctica, I really want to see a blue whale, which visits polar waters in the summer. In the winter it moves toward the equator — the great imaginary circle around the earth's middle. The blue whale is one of the largest living things in the world; only a few trees are bigger!
>
> Your Friend

What you do:

1. Cut out the whale from the blue construction paper. Glue the whale onto the stick. Use the black marker to draw on the whale's fins, eyes, and mouth. Use the blue marker to color the stick.

2. Glue construction paper onto the bottom of the tray for water. Cut a slit in the bottom of the tray.

3. Use the black marker to draw waves. Insert the stick into the slit to move the whale.

What you need:

- Blue construction paper
- Child safety scissors
- Popsicle stick
- White craft glue
- Blue and black markers
- Styrofoam tray (from fruits or vegetables only)

Penguin Playmates.
Another animal that lives in Antarctica is the southern elephant seal. Make elephant seals resting on an iceberg! Cut out four seal shapes. Take two and glue them together with a toothpick in between. Now, do the same thing with the other two pieces. Then, stick the toothpicks in an upside-down Styrofoam plate.

Learn More! To learn more about blue whales, read *Big, Blue Whale* by Nicola Davies and Nick Maland.

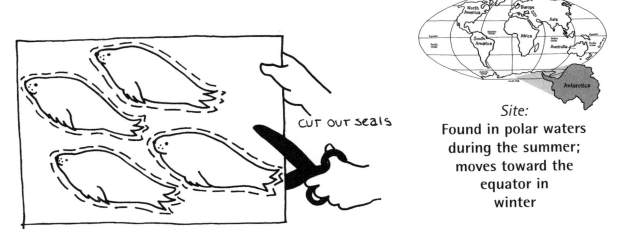

CUT OUT seals

Site:
Found in polar waters during the summer; moves toward the equator in winter

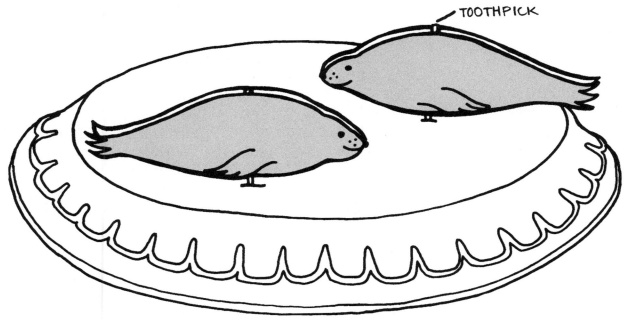

TOOTHPICK

Activity Index by Skill Level

Check the symbol at the beginning of each activity to quickly assess the challenge level.

Easy
(for even the littlest hands)

Clicking Castanet	80
Conical Hat	52
Decorated Egg	86
Desert Sand Dune	75
Didgeridoo	37
Giant Tortoise	107
Hatching Alligator	18
Icebergs	122
Loch Ness Monster	98
Masai Beaded Necklace	67
Musical Maraca	103
Reco-Reco	115
Totem Pole	26
Zulu Beehive Hut	73

Medium
(requires a few more steps)

Aboriginal Bark Painting	35
Ashanti Kente Cloth	77
Beautiful Lei	31
Blue Whale	124
Chinese Paper Fan	49
The Dinosaur "Sue"	20
Emerald Tree Boa Constrictor	109
Flamingo	58
Gaucho Belt	113
Giant Armadillo	117
Giant Sequoia	24
Gold Mask	105
Indian Elephant	56
Kiwi Bird	33
Korean Drum	44
Lion Mask	71

Matryoshka	88
Nile Crocodile	69
Orange Tree	60
Papel Picado	22
Passport	7
Postage Stamps	12
Royal Crown	96
Statue of Liberty Torch	14
Carved Stone Statue	111
Striped Zebra	65
Windmill	94
Worry Doll	101

Challenging
(more involved projects)

Adélie Penguin	120
Bactrian Camel	46
Bald Eagle	28
Castle	90
Eiffel Tower	82
The Great Pyramid	63
Japanese Doll	42
Kangaroo	39
Lotus Flower	54
The Little Mermaid	92
Spirit of St. Louis	16
Suitcase	8

More Good Books from Williamson Books

Little Hands® Books for Ages 2 to 7:

Parents' Guide Children's Media Award
Alphabet Art
With A to Z Animal Art & Fingerplays
BY JUDY PRESS

Parents' Choice Recommended Award
Animal Habitats!
Learning About North American Animals and Plants through Art, Science, and Creative Play
BY JUDY PRESS

Art Starts for Little Hands!
Fun & Discoveries for 3- to 7-year-olds
BY JUDY PRESS

Celebrate America
Learning About the USA Through Crafts and Activities
BY JILL FRANKEL HAUSER

Creating Clever Castles & Cars
(From Boxes and Other Stuff) Kids Ages 3–8 Make Their Own Pretend Play Spaces
BY MARI RUTZ MITCHELL

Parents' Choice Gold Award
Fun with My 5 Senses
Activities to Build Learning Readiness
BY SARAH. A. WILLIAMSON

Kindergarten Success
Helping Children Excel Right from the Start
BY JILL FRANKEL HAUSER

Parent's Guide Classic Award
LifeWorks Magazine Real Life Award
The Little Hands Art Book
Exploring Arts & Crafts with 2- to 6-year-olds
BY JUDY PRESS

The Little Hands Big Fun Craft Book
Creative Fun for 2- to 6-Year Olds
BY JUDY PRESS

Parents' Choice Approved
Little Hands Create!
Art & Activities for Kids Ages 3 to 6
BY MARY DOERFLER DALL

Parents' Choice Approved
Little Hands Paper Plate Crafts
Creative Art Fun for 3- to 7-Year-Olds
BY LAURA CHECK

American Bookseller Pick of the Lists
Math Play!
80 Ways to Count & Learn
BY DIANE MCGOWAN & MARK SCHROOTEN

Science Play!
Beginning Discoveries for 2- to 6-Year-Olds
BY JILL FRANKEL HAUSER

Sing! Play! Create!
Hands-On Learning for 3- to 7-Year-Olds
BY LISA BOSTON

Kids Can!® Books for Ages 7 to 14:

American Bookseller Pick of the List
Oppenheim Toy Portfolio Best Book Award
Skipping Stones Nature & Ecology
Honor Award
EcoArt!
Earth-Friendly Art & Craft
Experiences for 3- to 9-Year-Olds
BY LAURIE CARLSON

Keeping Our Earth Green
Over 100 Hands-On Ways to Help
Save the Earth
BY NANCY F. CASTALDO

Parent's Guide Children's Media Award
Kids' Art Works!
Creating with Color, Design, Texture & More
BY SANDI HENRY

American Bookseller Pick of the Lists
Dr. Toy Best Vacation Product
Kids' Crazy Art Concoctions
50 Mysterious Mixtures for Art & Craft Fun
BY JILL FRANKEL HAUSER

The Kids' Multicultural Art Book
Art & Craft Experiences from Around
the World
BY ALEXANDRA MICHAELS

Parents' Choice Approved
Skipping Stones Multicultural Honor Award
Benjamin Franklin Best Multicultural
Book Award
The Kids' Multicultural Cookbook
Food & Fun Around the World
BY DEANNA F. COOK

Parents' Choice Approved
The Kids' Multicultural Craft Book
35 Crafts from Around the World
BY ROBERTA GOULD

Kids Write!
Fantasy & Sci Fi, Mystery,
Autobiography, Adventure & More
BY REBECCA OLIEN

Leap into Space!
Exploring the Universe and Your Place in It
BY NANCY F. CASTALDO

Parents' Choice Recommended
Making Amazing Art!
40 Activities Using the
7 Elements of Art Design
BY SANDI HENRY

Using Color in Your Art
Choosing Colors for Impact & Pizzazz
BY SANDI HENRY

Wordplay Café
Cool Codes, Priceless Puzzles &
Phantastic Phonetic Phun
BY MICHAEL KLINE

Little Hands® and *Kids Can!*® are registered
trademarks of Ideals Publications.

To Order Books:
Toll-free phone orders with credit cards:
1-800-586-2572

We accept Visa and MasterCard *(please
include the number and expiration date)*.
Or, send a check with your order to:

Ideals Publications
Williamson Books Orders
2636 Elm Hill Pike, Suite 120
Nashville, TN 37214

For a free catalog: **mail, phone, or
fax (888-815-2759)**

Please add **$4.00** for postage for one
book plus **$1.00** for each additional
book. Satisfaction is guaranteed or full
refund without questions or quibbles.

Internet Marketing

THIRD EDITION

Charles F. Hofacl

FLORIDA STATE UNIVERSITY

 New York   Chichester   Weinheim   Brisbane   Toronto   Singapore

ACQUISITIONS EDITOR   Brent Gordon

MARKETING MANAGER   Jessica Garcia

PRODUCTION EDITOR   Ken Santor

COVER DESIGNER Harold Nolan

COVER PHOTO   Michael Agliolo/International Stock

This book was printed and bound by Malloy Lithographing. The cover was printed by Phoenix Color Corp.

The paper in this book was manufactured by a mill whose forest management programs include sustained yield harvesting of its timberlands. Sustained yield harvesting principles ensure that the numbers of trees cut each year does not exceed the amount of new growth.

ISBN 0-471-39051-8 (pbk)

Printed in the United States of America

10 9 8 7 6 5 4 3 2

Preface

In the past few years the Internet has gone through several phases, from obscurity through hype, all the way to being a simple fact of life today. Almost as soon as the Internet was privatized, marketers staked their turf and sought to use the medium to further the goals of their firms in various ways. While there are numerous books on the subject of marketing using the Internet, all tend to be practitioner-oriented and focus solely on computer nuts and bolts. *Internet Marketing* discusses many of those same nuts and bolts, but places them in the context of marketing strategy, consumer behavior, advertising, and the other business topics that make marketing different than computer programming.

In fact, the title of this textbook, *Internet Marketing*, neatly sums up the two disciplines it brings together. The book has both an Internet component and a marketing component. No doubt instructors will vary in terms of how much Internet coverage they will include in a course. This book is designed to let the instructor add as little or as much of the Internet component as he or she feels comfortable including. Wherever possible, the technical details of networked computing have been segregated to allow the instructor to omit them if desired. For example, when the HTML page-creation language is discussed in terms of its impact on the consumer, those discussions are circumscribed to a sidebar. In addition, Chapter 2, "What Exactly Is the Internet?," Chapter 5, "How to Create Web Pages," and Chapter 14, "The Mechanics of Electronic Commerce" can be skipped without any harm being done to the overall narrative.

The printed textbook is really just one-half of the materials for this course—the other half being a companion Web site which is also a critical component. The text and the associated Web site have been designed from the start to complement each other. While some books have supporting Web sites, the site and this book play a nearly-equal role in the case of *Internet Marketing*. Our aim in developing the set was to capitalize on the strength of each medium. Our goal in the design process was to use each medium for what it does best. The textbook most efficiently teaches the key concepts and provides a serial narrative on the topic. The interactivity of the Internet, on the other hand, makes it ideal for providing student activities of various sorts such as hypertext cases and homework questions. The Internet is also unsurpassed in its ability to point students to live examples of the main points. The dynamic nature and timeliness of online publishing makes it perfect for producing pointers to current events that relate to class materials. And finally, the purchase of *Internet Marketing* allows you four months of access to the nation's most-respected business news service: the *Wall Street Journal Interactive Edition*. We have provided chapter-specific research activities on the *Internet Marketing* Web site. By using the *Interactive Journal* to complete the exercises, you can gain a better understanding of the chapter topics and while becoming familiar with the features and strengths of the *Interactive Journal*.

This book is arranged into five sections. The first section provides an introduction to the Internet. Subsequent sections focus on communication, selling, content development and creation, and providing network functionality. The final section serves as a catch-all for several miscellaneous topics that don't clearly belong in any of the other sections.

We are grateful to a number of instructors and professionals from around the world for their helpful reviews of this second edition of Internet Marketing:

Reza Motameni, California State University, Fresno
Kim Sheehan, University of Oregon
Pola Gupta, University of Northern Iowa
John Beaumont-Kerridge, University of Luton
Glenn B. Voss, North Carolina State University
Kathleen S. Micken, Roger Williams University
Barbara Bart, Savannah State University
Edwin Tang, The Chinese University of Hong Kong
Donald Sciglimpaglia, San Diego State University
Paul Richardson, Loyola University
Margaret Kurko, College of the Siskiyous
Larisa Genin, Golden Gate University
Chantal Ladias, American College of Dublin
Michelle Nelson, Pacific University
Donna Green, University of Windsor
Mark Durkin, University of Ulster
Nanda Viswanathan, University of Redlands
Douglas Lowry, Franciscan University of Steubenville

I would like to thank the folks at Digital Springs, Inc. and John Wiley & Sons, including Rick Leyh, Steve Welch, Molly Saint-James, Camille McMorrow, Jeanne Payne, and Sara Schroeder of DSI and Brent Gordon and David Kear at JWS for all of their assistance. At first, they provided guidance in converting a set of class notes into a textbook, and more recently, in improving and updating a book. It is also important to thank the numerous busy faculty who took the time to review, and to make important suggestions for this edition. In addition, Kathy Micken has provided invaluable contributions to the *Internet Marketing* Web Companion.

I would like to thank my wife, Linda Vaughn, for her patience with my compulsion to be connected to the Internet anytime—day or night. I would also like to thank my parents, who as professional educators imparted to me the genuine thrill of learning. Jamie Murphy deserves thanks for numerous discussions about the topics included in this book. His ability to analyze the Internet, as well as his enthusiasm for doing so, is of the highest quality. And while I am thanking Jamie for his help with the book, I would like to thank him for acting as my cycling coach, although there are certain weeks . . . well, let me just leave it at "Thanks!"

CFH

Contents

Part I Introduction to Marketing on the Internet

CHAPTER 7 HUMAN INFORMATION PROCESSING OF WEB SITES

CHAPTER 8 WHAT A WEB SITE SHOULD LOOK LIKE

CHAPTER 9 WEB SITE COPY

CHAPTER 10 ADVERTISING BANNERS

Part III Computer-Mediated Selling

Part IV Providing Web Content

CHAPTER 15 THE CONTENT SITE VISITOR

CHAPTER 16 STRATEGIES FOR PROVIDING CONTENT

CHAPTER 17 LEGAL AND ETHICAL ISSUES

CHAPTER 18 WEB LOG DATA

Part V New Functions, New Businesses

CHAPTER 19 THE DIGITAL FUTURE

GLOSSARY 153

INDEX 157

Part I

INTRODUCTION TO MARKETING ON THE INTERNET

Chapter 1

CATEGORIES OF INTERNET MARKETING

LEARNING OBJECTIVES

1. Understand the different activities marketers engage in over the Internet.
2. Understand the following marketing activities: communicating, selling, providing content, and providing a network function.

The phrase *marketing on the Internet* is difficult to pin down because so many companies are performing so many different activities that could be described as Internet marketing. In order to get a handle on these activities, this book divides Internet marketing into four categories: communicating, selling, providing content, and providing a network function. These four categories constitute four of the five parts of this book; the first part is an introduction to the Internet. If Internet marketing can be divided into these four categories, it is often the case that any Web site may be engaging in two or more of these styles of marketing. For example, a Web site used for selling could also be used for communicating. Or a company's Web site might provide interesting content or "edutainment," both of which are interspersed with marketing communication about the product. Obviously, any one company or any one Web site could fall into multiple categories. Nonetheless, the four categories of marketing provide a convenient way to organize the book and to introduce the key concepts of Internet marketing.

Communication

Many businesses use the Internet to communicate with customers and potential customers. Compared to other media used for advertising or other forms of promotion, the Internet is especially useful for establishing and building relationships with customers. For example, Italian food producer Ragu includes recipes on its Web site, encouraging consumers to revisit the site whenever they might need a quick menu tip.

Various other Internet services such as email, email lists, Usenet, autoresponders and chat rooms can also be used to communicate with potential customers. Smart marketers study the culture and behavior of the target consumers using those services before proceeding haphazardly and looking foolish.

Selling

The Internet is experiencing booming growth in online selling, a new form of direct marketing that has emerged in large scale over the past several years. Firms that sell information-rich products like books (www.amazon.com), CDs (www.cdnow.com), financial services (www.eschwab.com), software (www.egghead.com), symbolic products like travel tickets (www.travelocity.com), and computers (www.dell.com) have seen rapid sales growth on the Internet. At a casual glance, one might think that the Internet will eliminate all channel intermediaries, or middlemen, and that the Internet will inevitably force marketers to keep prices as low as possible. In this section of the book, we will see that this is not necessarily so.

Providing Content

The *Content Site* represents a third category of marketing activity. To understand why a content site is different from the previous two categories, we might borrow a phrase from Nicholas Negroponte, who contrasts "atoms versus bits" in the book *Being Digital*. With the first two categories, communicating and selling, the whole point of using the Internet is to support the marketing of some physical product or service made up of atoms. Ragu wants to communicate about its food products and CD Now wants to ship you a CD. For both Ragu and CD Now, the Web site is an expense, either a promotion expense or a selling expense, and one that hopefully pays for itself through sales.

When a firm provides Internet content, the Web site itself, which is made up of bits not atoms, is not just an expense, it is the actual product. Many content sites are not associated with any physical product or service at all and are instead a completely *virtual* phenomenon. The site needs to pay for itself either through selling advertising or charging some sort of viewer fee. To provide one example, the Jumbo content site (www.jumbo.com) offers shareware, a category of software that can be downloaded and tried for free, to any and all comers. The site supports itself with banner ads on its pages. *Portal* sites provide a different sort of content—sites like Yahoo! (www.yahoo.com) serve as gateways to many sites, helping the visitor by providing organization and recommendations.

Provide a Network Function

A special sort of content site uses the Internet to provide some useful function for visitors. These sites use the network to facilitate access to content provided by someone else and execute some kind of computer processing or transaction for the consumer. For example, a site like www.ebay.com, which bills itself as "your personal trading company™" might offer use of its server hardware to host auctions where buyers and sellers can meet. eBay does not provide the content; it merely hosts these auctions and provides various support services. Or a site like www.dejanews.com might provide a set of disk drives and computers that let you search Usenet archives and posts new messages. The millions of people who post messages to Usenet, a type of bulletin board system discussed in a later chapter, are the content providers. eBay leverages the energy provided by those who wish to buy something and those who wish to sell something. Likewise, Dejanews thrives on the desires of those people wanting to write something and those wanting to read that which has been written.

One could argue that a network function site is just a special type of content site as described in the previous section. However, the various ways of using networked computers to provide consumer or business services can be so creative and unique, it qualifies as a separate category.

Overview of this Book

This book is separated into five sections. The first section provides an introduction to the Internet. Even before delving into any details, it is clear that the Internet reduces the relevance of time of day and deflates the importance of the physical location of consumers and firms. One of the most fundamental questions firms must ask is what markets they would like to try to serve. The reduction in the importance of where the consumer is will certainly affect the answer to this question for many, many companies. Subsequent sections discuss communications, sales, content development, and providing a network function. This last section also covers additional topics that do not fit into the earlier sections. As we have seen over the past few years, on Internet time, strategic windows of opportunity open and close in the blink of an eye. It is safe to predict that the Internet will create winners, and will leave behind losers.

Summary

1.   Marketing on the Internet can be broken into the following activities: Communicating, selling, providing content, and offering a network function.
2.   Marketers use Web sites and other network services to communicate with customers. The goal is to create a strong relationship with the consumer.
3.   The Internet can also be used as a direct channel to sell products or services.
4.   Some Web sites are not tied to any physical product or service but instead offer a purely digital information product.
5.   Companies have created new electronic services that are facilitated with networked computers.

Online Activities

Visit the companion Web site at www.wiley.com/college/hofacker for chapter summaries, examples, hypertext cases, homework assignments, text material updates, research exercises, and *Wall Street Journal Interactive Edition* access.

GO TO   http://www.wiley.com/college/hofacker

THE WALL STREET JOURNAL.

References

Brady, Regina, Edward Forrest and Richard Mizerski (1997*) CyberMarketing: Your Interactive Marketing Consultant.* Chicago: NTC Business Books.

Deighton, John (1996) The Future of Interactive Marketing, *Harvard Business Review*, 74 (November/December), 151-162.

Ellsworth, Jill H. and Matthew V. Ellsworth (1997) *Marketing on the Internet*, Second Edition, New York: John Wiley.

James, Geoffrey (1996) *Business Wisdom of the Electronic Elite*. Random House.

Janal, Daniel S. (1997) *Online Marketing Handbook*, Van Nostrand Reinhold.

Komenar, Margo (1997) *Electronic Marketing*, New York: John Wiley.

Negroponte, Nicholas (1995) *Being Digital*, New York: Vintage Books.

Peterson, Robert A. (1997) Electronic Marketing: Visions, Definitions and Implications, In Robert A. Peterson (Ed.), *Electronic Marketing and the Consumer*, Thousand Oaks: Sage.

Kalakota, Ravi and Andrew B. Whinston (1997) *Electronic Commerce: A Manager's Guide*, Reading, MA: Addison Wesley Longman,

Schwartz, Evan I (1997) *Webonomics*, New York: Broadway Books.

Tapscott, Don (1995) *The Digital Economy: Promise and Peril in the Age of Networked Intelligence*, New York: McGraw-Hill.

Vasos, Tom (1996) *Strategic Internet Marketing*, Indianapolis, IN: Que Press.

Zeff, Robbin and Brad Aronson (1997) *Advertising on the Internet*, New York: John Wiley.

Chapter 2

WHAT EXACTLY IS THE INTERNET?

LEARNING OBJECTIVES

1. Define what the Internet is.
2. Understand some of the ways the Internet differs from mass media.
3. Learn the history of the Internet and how that history affects the way it works today.
4. Learn about the Domain Name Service, DNS.
5. Understand the different speeds with which information moves across the Internet.

Over the past several years, you have probably seen or heard the word "Internet" thousands of times. You probably have already been using it for a while yourself and have a good idea of what the word means in practice. The Internet itself, though, is quite hard to define. It was created using computer software, and since software can be programmed to do almost anything, the Internet is flexible to the point of being difficult to pin down.

By strict definition,

> the Internet is the sum total of devices interconnected using the Internet Protocol.

The Internet Protocol is usually abbreviated IP. A protocol is simply a set of technical agreements or conventions specifying rules for creating services. The upshot here is that the definition of the Internet boils down to a set of devices using certain standards. There is no other requirement. The existence of IP has allowed developers to ignore specific hardware nuts and bolts and instead focus their energy on creating services of benefit to Internet users. Examples of these services would include email, chat, Usenet, and the World Wide Web.

Internet services are generally offered by one piece of software, called a *server*, for use by another, often called a *client*. Consequently the Internet is sometimes called a client-server system. If you have used the World Wide Web, you have used client software before. A Web browser like Microsoft® Internet Explorer or Netscape® Navigator is a client that you can use to request to view a

Web page. The server software has the job of sending you that page, and the client software has the job of receiving it and then putting it up on your screen within the window allotted to the client.

The word Internet is short for **Internetwork,** and many people shorten the whole thing to just "the Net." The prefix "inter-" is often used in English to refer to the connections between things, as in *inter*national. In the case of the word "international," we mean connections between nations. An internetwork is a connection between two or more networks. IP has rules to create a single *virtual* network from two or more real—meaning physical—networks. In other words, we experience the illusion of a single, seamless network using IP even though the various networks might use entirely different types of wires, fiber, or communications technologies.

IP is an **open protocol,** as compared to a **proprietary protocol.** No company owns the protocol in the way that Microsoft, for example, owns the Windows® operating system. IP standards are worked out in technical committees consisting of hardware and software vendors, users, and engineers.

The Internet is also an **open network**. In comparison, the network deployed by a cable or phone company is "closed." The Internet has no rules that say you are allowed, or are not allowed, to attach certain devices to it. And any device attached to the Internet is a network **peer**, which is to say it is one among equals. Of course, for that device to interoperate with the other stuff attached to the Net, it needs to know about IP. But that is the only rule.

There are major differences between an **interactive medium** like the Internet and **mass media** such as TV, magazines, billboards, or radio. Those media involve a unidirectional, or one to many, communication process. In contrast, the Internet enables a wide variety of communication patterns between firms and consumers and between consumers and other consumers. In the Internet we see a more active, less passive, consumer than with mass media. Rather than compare the Internet to a mass medium like broadcast radio, it can be instructive to think in terms of the telephone system. Like the phone network, the Internet is interactive and user-driven. Everybody has the opportunity to disseminate information.

The ability of Internet users to fully participate in the communications process produces new rules for marketing. The Internet has its own culture and a different set of expectations for communication. The consumers are in charge on the Internet. If they don't like your Web site, they can go somewhere else with the click of a button. It is also important to understand that the Internet tends to work best as a **pull medium**, not a **push medium** like TV. Television advertisements are pushed at viewers whether they want to look at them or not. Commercial breaks are the price the consumer pays to view shows. If viewers could avoid them, they usually would.

In contrast, think about how the Yellow Pages work. The consumer does not need to try to avoid the Yellow Pages. The consumer decides when to look at them and what page to go to. The Net is much more like the Yellow Pages than it is like TV. A successful Web page acts like a flower, pulling in the consumer who is like a bee searching for honey. Unlike TV, Internet communication does not intrude on the consumer.

A Brief History of the Internet

The Internet was created in 1969 as the result of a grant from the Advanced Research Projects Agency of the Pentagon. Initially used by computer scientists at only at a few large universities, the network was adopted by more and more academic departments within secondary learning institutions in the United States through the 1970s and 1980s. By the 1980s, the contribution of the United States federal government had passed from the Pentagon to the National Science Foundation (NSF), and in the early 1990s, the NSF made a decision to pass control of the Internet to the private sector.

Two key events preceded the adoption of the Internet by a large number of businesses in the mid–1990s. The first was the invention of the client-server system known as the World Wide Web by Tim Berners-Lee. Berners-Lee invented the hypertext transfer protocol (HTTP), which specifies exactly how a Web client, now usually called a browser, should ask for a page and how a Web server should send the page to the browser. HTTP also can be used to form a communications channel between the Web and other types of software. Berners-Lee also created the idea of the Uniform Resource Locator (URL). A URL is the way we specify the address of a document on the Web. Finally, he invented HTML, the Hypertext Markup Language used to create Web pages.

The World Wide Web married the idea of hypertext, in which the user could easily follow a "link" from one document to another, to the idea of networked computers, where any of these documents might be stored anywhere in the world. The concept of hypertext was anticipated in a Summer 1945 article in *Atlantic Monthly*, written by Vannevar Bush, a Vice President and Dean of Engineering at MIT. Bush contemplated a microfilm-based storage device that could be easily and quickly consulted. The actual phrase *hypertext* was invented by Ted Nelson in 1965 to describe how computers could be used to create non-sequential text.

Berners-Lee's original Web functioned using only plain text on large Unix® systems. The next major impetus to the growth of the Web was the programming and free distribution of Mosaic, one of the first World Wide Web clients to use a graphical user interface (GUI). Beginning in 1993, Mosaic was available for free for PCs, Macs and X-Windows workstations. Mosaic is closely associated with Marc Andreesen, who helped develop the software while at the National Center for Supercomputer Applications at the University of Illinois, and who is now with America Online's Netscape division. The Web in general and Mosaic in particular standardized and simplified the way in which Internet resources could be accessed—and sparked a wave of creativity that has yet to crest.

How the Internet Works

How do you design and control a massively complex network with tens of millions of computers? The simple answer is, you don't. It is important to keep in mind that no one "planned" the Internet. Even today, or perhaps especially today, no one controls the Internet. There is no "Internet, Inc." to set rules. In fact, the network is an international phenomenon that crosses numerous technical and political boundaries. There is no network control center, institution, company, or government in charge. In fact, the Internet has not actually been "built" in the sense that one builds a house or a watch. Its growth has had something of an organic quality. Watching the Internet change these past decades has not been like watching a work crew put up a building. It was more like watching vines spread across a field or watching a child grow up.

No one controls the Internet for the same reason that no one controls the economy. At this time, very few nations of the world centrally plan their economies. Instead, most economic decision making is distributed and tends to run from the bottom up rather than from the top down. Computers on the Internet work this way as well. The assemblage of electronics, copper, and fiber that we today know as the Net, acts more like a market, or perhaps an ecosystem, than a designed machine.

Communication over the Internet uses a technique known as **packet routing.** When you send email to someone, your message is broken down into small pieces called packets. Likewise, Web pages, chat messages, and video snippets are all chopped up into packets. Each packet has its destination written in a "header," similar to putting an address on an envelope.

The devices that move packets around the network are called **routers.** A router is a computer that is attached to two or more networks. When a router receives a packet containing part of your email, if that router knows the destination for that packet; it sends it there. If it doesn't know the destination, it sends the packet to some other router that it thinks might know the destination.

Consider the map of a simple internetwork (Figure 2.1) that connects networks A, B, C, D, and E. Network A is connected to network B because there is a router attached to both A and B. Similarly, there is a router which is attached to networks B, C, and D that allows those three networks to interoperate.

Now, if a person on network A wants to send email to a person on network E, the router on network A (which is also on network B) looks over those packets, decides they are not destined for anyone on network A, and sends them on to network B. The important fact here is that the router on network A doesn't need to know anything about networks C, D, and E. It only needs to know its immediate neighbors. If it doesn't recognize a destination, all it needs to know is to send the packet to network B. Next, network B receives the packet for network E. The router on network B might have a rule that says, "If you get something for network E, send it along to network D. But if the line to network D is busy or down, send it to network C instead."

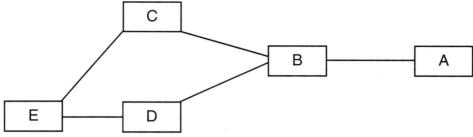

Figure 2.1—A Simple Internetwork

Eventually, all of the packets that constitute your email make their way to network E and your recipient. These packets are then reassembled in the correct order. Internet phone calls and video conferences work the same way. Despite the complexity of the Internet, or perhaps because of it, each router only needs to know about local conditions. To put this another way, the Internet itself is relatively dumb. The intelligence in the Internet is local; it resides in the computers that are attached to it.

Once again, let's compare the Internet to the telephone network. Even though both the phone network and the Internet are user-driven, unlike the Internet the phone network is a smart network. Phone companies have invested millions in many expensive switches that have a lot of computational power used to control the network. When you make a phone call, one or more of these switches checks for availability and reserves a circuit between you and your party for your sole use. The devices attached to the phone network—namely telephones—tend to be fairly dumb little gadgets that need to be completely controlled by the smart telephone network. In contrast, on the Internet, the network itself is dumb—it simply passes packets in the general direction of the smart computers those packets are addressed to.

Names on the Internet

Similar to the technique of packet routing described above, the naming system of the Internet is also decentralized. Routing is done using the numerical network address of the destination computer, known as its IP address. Every computer on the network has an IP address, which looks like four numbers separated by three dots. The software that translates the name of a machine to its IP address and vice versa is called the Domain Name System, or DNS.

Suppose someone in England wants to send email to a certain student living in a dorm called Annie Hall. Let's assume this student receives email at a computer named anniehall.bigu.edu. You might ask, "Is there a central authority that keeps track of all the names of all the Internet computers?" The answer is no, because such a solution would not **scale** well. In this context the word scale means that such a solution might break down if the network gets 10, 100, or 1,000 times bigger. In fact, it would not work even now; the Internet is already too big.

Instead of having one central name authority, there are "root" DNS servers that know the names of other DNS servers that know the answer. A computer housed at Big U and running DNS software would act as the DNS authority for anything under the "bigu.edu" name. This local machine would know the address for anniehall.bigu.edu and all the other machines on campus. No one else has to be an authority on Big U. The root servers just need to know the name of the Big U DNS server. The local Big U DNS server takes care of the details of how to find the machine called anniehall.

The Domain Name System is typical of the way the Internet works in the sense that it leverages decentralized, or local, intelligence. Some might call such a system "anarchistic." It is true that in a world where trademarks and company using names are zealously guarded, the anarchistic Internet approach using local decision making offers the possibility of litigation over who owns any given name. This will be discussed in more detail in Chapter 17. For now, it should be mentioned that you must register a domain name for your company. How one goes about doing this depends on what country you are in. In the United States, Network Solutions, Inc. (http://www.networksolutions.com) has been responsible for registering .com domains. The situation is changing however, with Network Solutions slated to lose its monopoly on business domain names shortly.

Network Speed

All information on a computer is stored in terms of numbers, and all numbers on a computer are ultimately stored as 1s and 0s. For example, the letter "A" is stored as 01000001. A picture might be stored as a much longer string of 1s and 0s that keep track of which part of the picture is which color.

Each 1 or 0 is called a **bit**. Internet communication speed is measured by the number of bits that can be transmitted per second.

People who access the Internet from work, or school, frequently do so on a computer that is directly attached to a local area network, or LAN. Different types of LANs run at different speeds, but LANs tend to be much faster than the type of connection people typically use at home, which are **modem** connections.

A modem is a device that allows a digital computer built within the last few years to successfully use the analog telephone network, which originates from the earlier part of the twentieth century. As a result, modems are quite a bit slower than LAN connections. Table 2.1 gives the speeds at which various devices connect computers to the Internet.

As technology changes, these numbers will change also. But one thing that will always be important is the number of significant digits. The fastest modems move Internet data at five-digit speed. The fastest LANs move data at nine-digit speed. Those four extra digits mean that a connection at work or school could be

Table 2-1
Internet Connection Speeds

Type of Connection	Speed of the Connection
Older Modem	14,400 bits per second
Typical Modem	28,000 bits per second
Newer Modem	56,000 bits per second
Digital Phone (ISDN)	64,000 bits per second
Cable Modem 3,000,000 bits per second	Ethernet LAN 10,000,000 bits per second
Fast Ethernet	100,000,000 bits per second

10,000 times faster than one at home. The speed of the consumer's connection has a big impact on what works and what does not work in marketing to that consumer. Of course describing what marketing tactics work on the Internet and which do not is the concern of most of the rest of this book.

Summary

1. The Internet is the sum total of devices interconnected using the Internet Protocol. The Internet Protocol is an open standard, and the Internet is an open network. The Internet is an interactive medium that is user driven.
2. The Internet is not controlled by any one company or government.
3. Three key events in the history of the Internet are the initial grant from the U.S. Defense Advanced Research Projects Agency, the invention of the World Wide Web to facilitate collaborative scientific writing, and the addition of a graphical user interface to the Web, which made Internet navigation a matter of pointing and clicking with a mouse.
4. Information moves from one computer to another using a technology called *packet routing*, which involves breaking the information into pieces and letting each piece make its own way from one part of the Internet to the next.
5. One computer can find another thanks to the domain name service that translates computer names into their numerical IP addresses and vice versa.
6. The speed with which consumers can receive information can vary by a factor of 10,000 or more, depending on what type of network access they have.

Online Activities

Visit the companion Web site at www.wiley.com/college/hofacker for chapter summaries, examples, hypertext cases, homework assignments, text material updates, research exercises, and *Wall Street Journal Interactive Edition* access.

GO TO   http://www.wiley.com/college/hofacker

 THE WALL STREET JOURNAL.

References

Anderson, Christopher (1995) The Accidental Superhighway, *The Economist*, July 1, 1995.

Bezian-Avery A, Calder B, Iacobucci D (1998) New media interactive advertising vs. traditional advertising, *Journal Of Advertising Research,* 3 (4), 23-32.

Brannback, Malin (1997) Is the Internet Changing the Dominant Logic of Marketing? *European Management Journal*, 15 (December), 698-707.

Cutler, Blayne (1990) The Fifth Medium, *American Demographics*, 12 (June), 24-29.

Day, George, (1998) Organizing for Interactivity, *Journal of Interactive Marketing*, 12 (Winter), 47-53.

Dimmick, John W., Jaspreet Sikand and Scott J. Patterson (1994) The Gratifications of the Household Telephone: Sociability, Instrumentality and Reassurance, *Communication Research*, 21 (October), 643-663.

Hafner, Katie and Matthew Lyon (1996) *Where Wizards Stay Up Late*. New York: Simon and Schuster.

Hanson, W., (1998) The Original WWW: Web Lessons From the Early Days of Radio, *Journal of Interactive Marketing*, 12 (Summer), 46-56.

Hoffman, Donna L and Thomas P. Novak (1996) Marketing in Hypermedia Computer-Mediated Environments: Conceptual Foundations, *Journal of Marketing*, 60 (July), 50–68.

Leong, Elaine K.F, Xueli Huang and Paul-John Stanners (1998) Comparing the Effectiveness of the Web site with Traditional Media, *Journal of Advertising Research*, (September/October), 44-51.

Pattinson, Hugh, Linden Brown (1996) Chameleons in Marketspace: Industry Transformation in the New Electronic Marketing Environment," *Journal of Marketing Practice: Applied Marketing Science*; 2 (1), 7-21.

Perse, Elizabeth M. and John A. Courtright (1993) Normative Images of Communication Media: Mass and Interpersonal Channels in the New Media Environment, *Human Communication Research,* 19 (June), 485-503.

Stewart, David W. and Scott Ward (1994) Media Effects on Advertising, in Jennings Bryant and Dolf Zillmann (eds.), *Media Effects: Advances in Theory and Research*, Hillsdale, New Jersey: Lawrence Erlbaum Associates.

Venkatesh, Alladi (1996) Computers and Other Interactive Technologies for the Home, *Communications of the ACM*, 39 (December), 47-54.

Chapter 3

WEB BROWSER SOFTWARE

LEARNING OBJECTIVES

1. Learn how a World Wide Web browser works.
2. Understand the importance of URLs.
3. Become familiar with a Web browser.

To market to consumers on the Internet, you need to know at least as much as they do about surfing the Web! This section discusses the use of a Web browser. The World Wide Web (WWW) is one of the most popular Internet services. As discussed in Chapter 2, there are two components to the WWW service: a client and a server. A WWW client is usually called a browser. You run a WWW client on your desktop machine. Examples include Netscape Navigator and Microsoft Internet Explorer. The role of a Web client is to retrieve information for you and present it on your screen.

The second component, the server software, usually runs on a more powerful computer that is connected to the Internet 24 hours a day, 7 days a week. Server software waits until a request for a page comes in, then sends the page across the network to the browser that requested it. Since visitors can request a page at any hour of the day or night, the computer running the server software is usually not turned off at the end of the day. Since you don't want to disappoint any potential customers, such computers are protected from power loss with backup batteries and from disk drive failure with disk drive redundancy. These machines are connected to the Internet at a much faster speed than a typical desktop machine that relies on a modem.

Despite these details, there really aren't that many differences between the kind of computer you might have on your desk and one that would run a Web server. A low-end desktop computer acting as a Web server could easily handle hundreds of thousands of visitors per week. If you had a permanent Internet connection, you could use almost any recently made computer as a server. Such a machine might prove sufficient for a small business entering the online world.

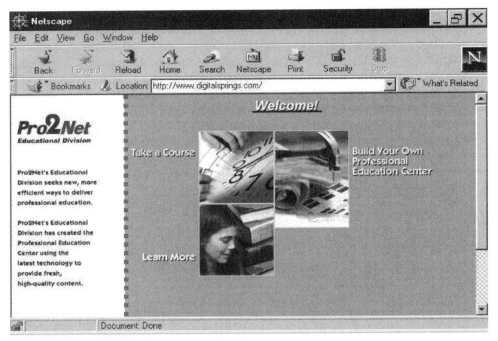

Figure 3.1—Web Browser Window

Figure 3.1 is a screen shot taken from a Web browser. The top part of the browser is the title bar. Below that is the menu bar. If you click with the left button of a mouse on a word in the menu bar, a menu of options will appear below that word. Below the title bar comes the tool bar, which contains shortcuts to many of the popular options appearing under the menu bar. Below the tool bar, the fourth line of the browser contains the location window that shows the address of the Web page being viewed.

A Web page is a hypertext document that might consist of text or pictures or sounds. In a hypertext document, some part of the screen is "hot," or "live". The live parts of the screen are usually called "hyperlinks," or just "links." Clicking with the left mouse button on a hyperlink brings related information to the screen. The related information might be from a different part of the same Web page, it might be on a different page on the same Web server, or it might be on a different computer altogether. The consumer clicks on these links to move around on the Web, part of a process that is called Web **navigation**.

There are several ways of navigating, but clicking on hyperlinks is one of the easiest. You can also type a Web page address into the location window, use the back arrow button on the tool bar, or use the items listed under the Netscape

Navigator Go option on the menu bar (which return you to sites you've been during your present session). This same function is provided by the Internet Explorer menu bar under the File option.

The address for a Web page is called a URL, which stands for Uniform Resource Locator. For example, the URL for the web companion of this book is

/http://www.wiley.com/college/hofacker

URLs are part of the language used to create Web pages. This language is called HTML, which stands for the Hypertext Markup Language. Web URLs begin with "http://" and then proceed to the domain name of the page. Sometimes there is another slash at the end followed by further information. This further information provides the file name of a page. If no file name is specified, the Web server assumes you want to look at a file called index.html.

Domain names are managed by the "Domain Name System," or DNS, a service described in some detail in Chapter 2. These domain names are read from right to left. DNS is a hierarchical system. The hierarchy means that the Internet's naming system, or its name space, as computer scientists would put it, is like a tree. There is a root to the tree, which serves as the main trunk, and then this main trunk splits into the main branches that form the right-most part of the domain name: .com, .edu, .net, .org, .uk, and a large number of others. As you go from right to left, the name gets more and more specific.

As an example, consider the name "garnet.acns.fsu.edu." This name resides within the ".edu" domain, meaning its name ultimately goes under the category of educational institutions. Moving to the left, the "fsu.edu" part of the name—in other words, the fsu.edu domain—refers to a specific institution; "acns" stands for Academic Computer and Network Services, which is a specific department at FSU. Finally, the name "garnet" can be tied to a specific computer belonging to that department.

Other Menu Bar Highlights

There are some useful items that appear under the menu bar that Internet marketer should understand. For one, the View menu bar heading contains an item called "Page Source" (Navigator) or simply "Source" (if you are using Internet Explorer). This option is very useful if you want to look at the HTML commands that underlie the appearance of a page.

Another important menu option can be found under the File option of the menu bar. To read a page that resides on your own computer, you can use the File "Open Page" option (on Internet Explorer this option is labeled simply "Open"). To save a copy of a page you are looking at you can use the "Save As" option of the File menu bar item.

Both Internet Explorer and Netscape Navigator allow the consumer to store the address of a Web site they would like to return to. With Netscape Navigator, this option can be found under the Communicator menu bar item as the "Bookmarks" option. Often a bookmark button can be found on the location bar on Netscape. On the Internet Explorer menu bar, this same item is labeled "Favorites." Consumers use the bookmarks or favorites capability to help them remember how to go back to their favorite places on the Web. Needless to say, there is a tremendous advantage to your firm if many consumers bookmark your site so that they can easily return to it. Getting your site into this coveted position is discussed in several places in the chapters ahead, but specifically in Chapter 16.

Summary

1. The Web browser is the client software for the World Wide Web Internet service.
2. The browser has a title bar, menu bar, tool bar and location bar.
3. Navigation on the Web can be performed by clicking on a hypertext link, using the back arrow, typing in a Web address, or using menu bar commands.
4. A Web page address is called a Uniform Resource Locator, or URL. A domain name can be part of a URL.
5. There are a variety of useful options on the menu bar, including the ability to view the source HTML for a page, save or open a local file, and store favorite URLs for later visits.

Online Activities

Visit the companion Web site at www.wiley.com/college/hofacker for chapter summaries, examples, hypertext cases, homework assignments, text material updates, research exercises, and *Wall Street Journal Interactive Edition* access.

GO TO   http://www.wiley.com/college/hofacker

WSJ.com **THE WALL STREET JOURNAL.**

Part II

COMMUNICATING

WITH CONSUMERS ONLINE

Chapter 4

Using the Internet to Communicate

Learning Objectives

1. Understand the various services available on the Internet, including the World Wide Web, email, email lists, Usenet, and Internet Relay Chat.
2. Understand some of the cultural "do's and don'ts" of these services, especially email lists and Usenet.

The Internet offers several different kinds of software service to its users. In this chapter we will discuss five of these: the World Wide Web, email, email lists, Usenet, and Internet Relay Chat. Researchers who have studied previous generations of communications media have concluded that consumers choose to use various services according to the gratifications received from those services. These gratifications do not just include the messages received. Indeed, the ability of a service to offer social interaction and diversion can be just as important to the consumer. These services differ in the way they offer content, interaction and fun.

The World Wide Web

The World Wide Web is a software system comprised of servers and clients. A client—or browser, as it is known—initiates a request for a document that is then sent to the client by a server. The client then formats the document for the user's screen. Often documents contain hypertext where a part of the screen is linked to other documents.

Marketers use the Web to convey promotional messages or interesting or informative information to consumers. The Web can also be used to sell products directly to the consumer, or to provide consumers with various computing or communication services. Since most of this book is concerned with marketing using the World Wide Web, for now we will look at some of the other Internet tools that can be used for marketing. The bulk of the remaining chapters deal with the Web.

Email

Electronic mail is a system by which documents can be sent from one Internet user to another. Sending email is similar to writing a letter on a word processing program. But unlike word processing software, email programs have additional features such as a send button or command that causes a copy of the document to be sent to another computer.

Email uses a "store and forward" principle. That means that the recipient of the email does not have to be logged on at the same time as the sender. The word **asynchronous** is used to describe this type of communication. Such a feature makes email very convenient as a cross between the telephone and postal mail. Telephone conversations have the property of "immediacy." But the telephone requires that both parties be on the line at the same time. If you have ever had to play "phone tag" by leaving and receiving messages on an answering machine, you know how inconvenient this requirement is. Postal mail, like email, is asynchronous but it is quite slow. Email, as a form of asynchronous communication that is very fast, would seem to have the best of both worlds.

One innovative use of email is to create an **autoresponder**. An autoresponder is a program that can reply to consumer email requests for information without any human intervention. While many consumers might prefer to use the Web, or to call an 800 number, to gather information, autoresponders typify the notion that a responsive firm, interested in growing the relationship between it and the consumer, uses every communications mechanism at its disposal.

Since email primarily consists of text, it is a somewhat formal medium. The same rules of grammar and spelling that apply to traditional written communication also apply to email when it is used for business. Any sales or marketing representative of a company using email to communicate with a potential customer needs to communicate clearly, grammatically, and with good spelling to maintain a positive image of the company and its offerings.

Email is written, digital, and potentially public communication. If the recipient chooses to save it, your email can hang around for a long time. It is also possible that the recipient might pass your email along to others, or even post your email on a bulletin board in the office or on an electronic bulletin board of some kind on the Internet. Always be careful to watch what you say, how you say it, and to whom you say it. It is not a bad idea to always double-check the "to:" address field before you send an email. It is quite common for people to send a personal message to the wrong individual by accident, with embarrassing (or worse) consequences.

Most email systems have some kind of "reply" button or command, which allows you to respond to an email you have received. The reply command can be used to quote a previous message. Often quoting is signified with the greater-than symbol (>). It is considered polite to quote just enough of an email to remind the original sender of the nature of the discussion. Over-quoting or failing to quote can be considered breaches of **netiquette**.

Netiquette is a system of social grace on the Internet. It is very important that sales and marketing specialists using the Internet be fully aware of netiquette and the do's and don'ts of Internet communication. Observing netiquette is especially critical when there is a large audience for a message, such as is the case with email lists.

Email Lists

An email list is a collection of individuals interested in communicating on a particular topic. These individuals are often referred to as subscribers. There are two email addresses for an email list.

The **address for the list**—If you send email to this address, everyone who is on the list will receive your email.

The **address for the server**—This address is used for administrative purposes such as subscribing or unsubscribing to the list.

It is very important to understand the distinction between these two addresses. If you send an administrative command to the address for the list instead of the address for the server, you and your company could be exposed to some embarrassment.

An email list provides a good metaphor for the way communication works on the Internet. We can illustrate this by considering a hypothetical email list called "boating–list" for people interested in discussing boats. If you work for a company that sells boats, you might have a piece of information of interest to the subscribers of boating list. If you sent an email to the address for the list, every subscriber gets the email. Your effort and cost remain the same whether one person receives your email or whether one million and one receive it. The cost is identical in either case.

Electronic communication generally tends to work this way. A communication effort may have a one-time start-up cost such as the cost of your salary during the time you were writing the email. Economists call this a fixed cost since your company has to pay this same fixed amount whether one or one million people see your note. But there is a very low marginal cost. The marginal cost of communication is the cost your firm must pay for each additional person who reads your note. Since you just have to send the email to one address, namely the address for the list, the marginal cost in this case is zero. If one extra person gets added to the subscription list, you still just have to send the email to one address, the address for the list. It all looks the same to you and your firm.

Now compare the cost structure of electronic communication to the situation with direct mail. In that case, every time you send out a piece to a new reader, you have to pay for additional postage and an envelope. The marginal cost is not zero. As the number of recipients goes up, the cost goes up. To a large extent, as the number of electronic readers go up, the cost stays flat.

Even though there may not be much of a cost to send an email to an email list, there may be a big penalty in consumer attitudes towards the firm if netiquette is violated. Some things that Internet users do not like include the following:

Spamming—The ire of subscribers is invariably raised when a marketer sends an email advertisement or a blatant promotion to the list address. Such email is called **spam**. Internet users do not appreciate intrusive ads. The natural pattern of informational flow in a user driven environment like the Internet is different than the flow of information that exists in the mass media. The Internet is best used as a communications channel to pull the consumer in. For many reasons it is not well suited for pushing unwanted ads on to the consumer. On the other hand, companies sometimes set up **opt-in** email lists. In an opt-in list, the consumer agrees to receive information or ads by email. Rather than trying to force an unwanted message on an unwilling audience, opt-in lists can enhance the relationship between the consumer and the firm, a topic which will be further explored in terms of the Web in Chapter 6. Some other important aspects of netiquette appear below:

Shouting—Posting a message in all uppercase is called shouting and is considered childish and argumentative.

Flaming—In email, vocal inflection is lost, which can lead to misunderstandings as well as unnecessary hostility and arguments. The worst case occurs if several parties escalate the conversation into an all out "flame war." Remember that what you say on an email list is very public. Even if you disagree with some consumer, don't embarrass yourself or your company by displaying impolite contempt for that person.

Off-topic Postings—Many subscribers take the purpose of the list seriously. Posting comments that are not about the subject at hand can cause people to get angry with you and your company.

One-on-one Discussions—It is considered a breach of netiquette to engage in a one-on-one conversation with another list member using the list address. To communicate with a specific individual or set of individuals, explicitly type in the email address for that individual or individuals.

Me-too Postings—Avoid chiming in with messages that quote another subscriber and that simply say "I agree."

When you subscribe to an email list, it is not a bad idea to **lurk** for a while. In this context lurking is not a bad thing; it just means that you soak up the conversation and learn the rules before speaking. Of course, be careful to read up on any policies of the list with regards to advertising. When you subscribe to a list you will probably receive some kind of statement or **Frequently Asked Questions (FAQ)** document.

An astute marketer will also wait to observe the tone of the conversation, the unwritten rules of the group, the topics typically discussed and other aspects of the group dynamic before entering the conversation and trying to sell something. An email list is not unlike a conversation at a party. You don't simply walk up to a group of people and try to start selling them on your company. If any of the subscribers wants to learn about your company, it is possible to let them know how to reach you with a certain amount of discretion, such as using a signature or **sig file**. A signature file is a bit of text added to outgoing email. A very common technique is to include your company's Web address as part of your signature, along with a one-line description of the firm. Then if somebody on the list needs help with a problem and has asked a question to the group, you may be able to answer that question by posting a reply back to the list address. There at the bottom of your email for all to see is the company URL of the knowledgeable person who helped. It is a subtle way of advertising and allows you to operate within the Internet "gift culture", so called because people using the Internet frequently act very generously.

Email lists are either **moderated** or **unmoderated**. A moderated list is one in which an individual, commonly called a moderator, controls which submitted messages actually go out to the list address for all subscribers to see. In an unmoderated list, anything that anybody posts automatically goes out to the list address. In either case, the moderator or the list owner should be consulted if you have any doubts at all about the appropriateness of a posting. The people who run lists often do so with no compensation as a service to the community around which the list is organized. You can't expect a list owner to be sympathetic to your marketing goals if you don't follow the rules of the list. While it may be possible to circumvent the list rules, since some of the software used to administer email lists is fairly primitive, you do so at the risk of your and your company's reputation.

There are two ways to receive an email list: **digest** or **mail** format. With digest format, the messages are sent to the subscriber in a batch after they have built up for a while. In mail format, you receive the messages one at a time as they are sent. When replying to a digest of messages, you need to be careful when you quote, that you don't quote everybody's messages. You need to be careful to specify a subject line that informs other readers about the nature of your posting.

We find a number of common shorthand conventions used on email lists such as the smiley. A smiley often looks like: :-) . It uses the keyboard characters to imitate a sidewards face. You can use a semicolon to create a winking appearance ;-), and using the left parenthesis produces a frown, as in :-(. Net users also tend to use various acronyms like **IMHO** (in my humble opinion), **BTW** (by the way), **YMMV** (your mileage may vary) and **TIA** (thanks in advance).

Usenet

Usenet is a shared system of topical conversation consisting of more than 50,000 discussion areas. Each discussion area is called a group or a **newsgroup**. A typical example might be "rec.bicycles.racing." These names are created hierarchically. Topics under "rec" are about recreation; topics under bicycles are about bicycles, naturally. You access newsgroups through a Usenet client that may be part of your email client since Usenet and email are somewhat similar. The difference is that email goes to you. With Usenet, the conversation is taking place in a public space, sort of like a bulletin board placed in a park for all to see. You go to it; it doesn't go to you. Messages posted to Usenet are often referred to as **articles**. The number of articles posted to Usenet newsgroups in the United States alone is more than 1,000,000 per day. While the rules for marketing on Usenet are similar to those for marketing on email lists, the differences between Usenet and email lists goes beyond the terminology of "groups" and "articles."

One subtle difference between email lists and Usenet is one of accountability. Email lists have an owner, and the computer processing that makes email lists happen is ultimately traceable. The address of the list must obviously be tied to a certain domain name. And since someone has to pay a registration for every domain name, there is connection there between real and virtual worlds. Newsgroups, on the other hand, are a cooperative venture among a very large number of Internet services organizations, around 2,500 in the US alone. Responsibility for keeping Usenet running is shared by thousands and thousands of technical people who receive the **newsfeed** and pass it along to another site. The Usenet communications channel is therefore not so closely connected to the offline world. Most importantly, the content that appears on Usenet is not controlled (nor is it remotely controllable) by any organization or set of organizations. In the anarchy that is the Internet, Usenet manages to stand out by being even less disciplined than the rest of the Net. So of course within this conversation, with its daily ocean of billions of bytes per day, there appear streamlets of pornography, racist ranting, and illegally copied intellectual property including music, pictures and software. Just as a vendor would not want to locate a retail outlet next to a dump, an online marketer needs to be wary of becoming associated with some of the marginal online behavior that occurs on Usenet.

Internet Relay Chat and Other Services

Internet Relay Chat is often abbreviated IRC. IRC is a real time, or synchronous, method of conversation by typing. IRC is very popular among younger Internet users who sometimes use it for hours at a time. Marketers can use the IRC service to gather consumers together for things like brainstorming or a focus group research session. A very similar method of performing online chat can be done using various Web-based products, as well as products called instant messaging. What IRC, Web based chat and instant messaging have in common is that all of the parties to the conversation must be online at the same time. They differ slightly in that with IRC you must go to a special server, known appropriately enough as an IRC server, in order to communicate with others. Web chat requires that you visit a specific Web page used to host the chat. Instant messaging requires that you specifically look for an individual you wish to chat with. In addition to chat, there are various real time games that can be played by Net subscribers who can symbolically take on various roles. These games go under such names as Multi-User Dungeons (MUDs). In these sorts of environments, it is possible to interact with others within a cloak of anonymity, being someone different than who you are from 9 to 5, face to face. As bandwidth increases, we can expect the popularization of new services that allow voice conversation as well as real and animated video. Marketing services that do not exist yet may be created by tomorrow's entrepreneurs to hep people have fun with others all over the world.

Summary

1. Email is store-and-forward asynchronous communication.
2. Email lists allow many recipients to receive the same message.
3. Usenet acts like a virtual bulletin board where individuals can post messages to other readers.
4. IRC allows people to communicate minute-by-minute as in a real chat.
5. There are rules for behavior on the Internet called netiquette.

Online Activities

Visit the companion Web site at www.wiley.com/college/hofacker for chapter summaries, examples, hypertext cases, homework assignments, text material updates, research exercises, and *Wall Street Journal Interactive Edition* access.

GO TO   http://www.wiley.com/college/hofacker

THE WALL STREET JOURNAL.

References

Angell, David and Brent Heslop (1994) *The Elements of Email Style*, Reading, MA: Addison-Wesley.

Berge, Zane (1994) Electronic Discussion Groups, *Communication Education*, 43 (2), 102-111.

Ha, Louisa (1995) Subscribers' Behaviors in Electronic Discussion Groups: A Comparison Between Academics and Practitioners, *Proceedings of the First Annual Conference on Telecommunications and Information Markets*, Newport, Rhode Island, November 5-8, 1995.

Newhagen, John E. and, Sheizaf Rafaeli (1996) Why Communication Researchers Should Study the Internet: A Dialogue, *Journal of Communica-tion*, 46, 4-13.

Nicovich, Stef, and T. Bettina Cornwell (1999) An Internet Culture: Implications for Marketing, *Journal of Interactive Marketing*, 12 (4), 22-33.

Ogan, Christine (1993) Listserve Communication During the Gulf War: What Kind of Medium is the Electronic Bulletin Board? *Journal of Broadcasting and Electronic Media*, 17 (3), 369-392.

O'Keefe, Gina J. and B. K. Sulanowski (1995) More Than Just Talk: Uses, Gratifications, and the Telephone, *Journalism and Mass Communications Quarterly*, 72, 922-933.

Okleshen C., and S. Grossbart (1998) Usenet Groups, Virtual Community and Consumer Behaviors, *Advances in Consumer Research*, 25, 276-282.

Schmitz, Joseph and Janet Fulk (1991) Organizational Colleagues, Media Richness and Electronic Mail, *Communication Research,* 18 (4), 487-523.

Sivadas E., R. Grewal and J. Kellaris (1998) The Internet As a Micro Marketing Tool: Targeting Consumers Through Preferences Revealed In Music Newsgroup Usage, *Journal of Business Research,* 41 (3), 179-186.

Sterne, Jim (1996) *Customer Service on the Internet*, New York: Wiley.

Turkle, Shelly (1995) *Life on the Screen: Identity in the Age of the Internet.* Simon and Schuster.

Venkatesh, Alladi (1998) Virtual Spaces as Consumer Environments: Theoretical and Applied Issues, *Advances in Consumer Research,* 25, 60-61.

Chapter 5

HOW TO CREATE A WEB PAGE

LEARNING OBJECTIVES

1. Understand how the Hypertext Markup Language, or HTML, works.
2. Learn some simple HTML commands.
3. Learn what types of software can be used to produce HTML.
4. Learn why it is important to have fast loading images.
5. Understand the fundamentals of computer image processing.
6. Learn how to make images look good and load quickly.

Hypertext Markup Language

Web pages are created using **HTML**, the Hypertext Markup Language. A markup language is a set of computer commands that indicate how the text and images for a page should be displayed. For example, to create a paragraph break in the sample below, I would insert the <p> symbol but not an actual paragraph break

```
This is paragraph one.<p>This is paragraph two.
```

A person looking at this page using a Web browser would see:

This is paragraph one.

This is paragraph two.

The browser does not show the "<p>" markup to the reader. Instead, it will create a paragraph break in the position that the "<p>" markup appears. In effect, you are programming the visitor's Web browser to display the text the way you want it to appear. The browser will automatically flow text into a single paragraph unless you act to explicitly prevent it from doing so by using some kind of markup like <p>.

There are two different types of programs you can use to create Web pages with HTML. The first approach is to use a "What you see is what you get"

(WYSIWYG) page creator such as Netscape Composer™ or Microsoft FrontPage® product. These products hide the HTML from you and insert it in the page automatically. Popular word processing programs, like Microsoft Word, will also create HTML documents for you. Word will let you save any word processing document in HTML format. To do this, you need to use the File menu item on the menu bar. Pick the "Save as HTML…" option off of the File menu.

A second option is to use another type of program known as an HTML editor. HTML editors do not hide the HTML from you but instead allow you to control the appearance of a page explicitly by typing in the HTML yourself. You can actually use any type of editor that will create an ASCII (plain text) file to create a Web page. For example, the Notepad processor that comes with Windows will save an ASCII file for you. Generally speaking, WYSIWYG page creators work well for simple pages and are much easier to learn than HTML editors, which require you have a knowledge of HTML. But to really control how a page looks, you need to enter the HTML yourself, or at least modify it yourself using an HTML editor.

Once you have created a page, it ordinarily needs to be **published**. Publishing is the word used to describe the process by which the page is made available to the millions of Internet visitors just dying to learn about your company. In general terms, the page needs to be stored on a disk available to a computer running Web server software. Depending on your situation, you may need to use an Internet service called **FTP**. This acronym stands for the File Transfer Protocol. FTP is used to move files like Web pages from one computer; like the one you use to create the page; to another; like the computer running the Web server software. You may not need FTP however, if the software you are using to create the page has direct access to the server's disk.

Some Basic Markups

All Web pages must follow the same basic sequence. A prototype page is presented below:

```
<!doctype html public "-//W3C//DTD// HTML 3.2 //EN">
<html>
<head>
<title>This part will appear on the title bar</title>
</head>
<body>
The content that will appear on the page goes here.
</body>
</html>
```

As you can see, all pages must being with a markup that looks like:

```
<!doctype html public "-//W3C//DTD// HTML 3.2 //EN">
```

Next, comes the <html> markup. If you look at the very bottom of the example, you will see a </html> markup. This illustrates the fact that some markups occur in matched pairs. The <html> markup opens, or begins the HTML section of the page and the </html> markup closes, or ends that section.

There are two parts to every Web page: the <head> section and the <body> section. With the exception of the <title> markup, almost all of what the viewer sees is contained within <body> and </body>.

The head section includes the <title> markup (as well as some other markups not detailed here). Note that the text appearing within the confines of <title> and </title> will not appear on the page itself. Instead, the title goes to the top margin of the browser which is called the title bar. The text appearing between <title> and </title> is also saved along with bookmarks, or favorites.

Now lets return to the <p> markup. This command has some subcommands, often called **parameters**, that you can optionally use. To center a paragraph, you can use <p align=center>. To align the paragraph with the right margin, you can use <p align=right>. To end centering or alignment, you must include a </p> markup.

The <br> markup creates a line break, meaning that any text or images following the <br> markup will appear beginning in the left margin of the next line.

You can control the appearance of words with several markups. The <em> markup is used for emphasis, while <strong> is used for strong highlighting. These two markups need beginning and end points. For example, if I wanted to emphasize the word cold, I might format the following sentence as shown: "Today will be very <em>cold</em>." Note how the </em> markup is used to close or end the emphasis.

How do you create a link to another page or to another site? Hyperlinks are creating using the anchor markup, <a>. The anchor markup is one of those commands that requires a closing markup in the form of a </a>. It also has one important subcommand, the href= parameter. To illustrate the anchor markup, let's say I wanted to link to the Weather Channel's Web site, www.weather.com. On my page, I want the phrase "cold and rainy" to be highlighted. When the visitor clicks on this phrase, I want them to then go visit the weather site. The form of the hypertext would appear as below:

```
Today will be <a href="http://www.weather.com/">cold and rainy</a>.
```

What the visitor would see would be:

Today will be <u>cold and rainy.</u>

As you can see, the phrase "cold and rainy" serves as the anchor for the link, which is then clickable. The anchor is identified as the part of the document between the <a> and the </a> markups. The href= parameter of the <a> markup serves to identify the page you want to link to. You use href to specify the URL of the page you want the visitor to see if they click on the anchor.

If you are linking to a page on the same server, you can leave off most of the URL. For example, maybe you are creating a page for www.bigcompany.com and you want to link to x.html, which is on the same server. The **fully qualified address** for x.html is http://www.bigcompany.com/x.html. But if the page you are working on is also on the server for www.bigcompany.com, the href could simply be href="x.html".

To insert an image into a page, use the <img> markup. For example, to insert the image file bigpic.gif into a page, you would use <img src="bigpic.gif">. Here I am assuming that the image of interest is contained in the image file called bigpic.gif.

It is important to keep track of the nesting of HTML commands. The concept of nesting can be illustrated by assuming you wanted to have the phrase "watch your nesting" bold and italicized. The first form below is preferable to the second:

```
You should <b><i>watch your nesting</i></b>

You should <i><b>watch your nesting</i></b>
```

Note that in the second instance, the <i> markup is no longer nested within the <b> markup. Inconsistent nesting can confuse the viewer's' browser when it goes to display the page on the screen.

Fast Computer Graphics

Web graphical images considerably enhance Web pages, making them more exciting and more compelling. An image can quickly convey an emotional tone and also display a huge amount of information. But it takes a lot of bandwidth to send an image via the Web. The concept of bandwidth was described in Chapter 2, but to briefly review, bandwidth is a measure of the speed with which computerized information can be sent from one place to another. Since all computerized information is represented as a series of one's and zero's, or bits, bandwidth is measured in bits per second. Many users access the Internet using modems, and many modems still in use today run at only 28,800 bits per second. Such a slow modem means that a page with large images, or with many images, can take a long time to load on the visitor's computer. The visitor may grow tired of waiting and give up, or visit another page instead of loading your page. Surveys have shown that slow loading pages are an ongoing complaint among Web users. Consequently, one of the main themes of this section is how to produce good-looking but fast-loading graphics for pages.

A computer screen is composed of individual dots, called **pixels**. Each dot is created by projecting a combination of three colors: red, green and blue. Unlike mixing paints, mixing computer colors is additive. With paints, mixing red, green, and blue would produce a dark color. On a computer screen, red, green and blue is white. Another difference between computers and other graphical media is that a computer screen has only 72 dots per inch. Photographs or paper can have far more than this, so when you scan artwork or photos for use on the Web, you should remember to set the scanner to 72 dots per inch.

In technical terms, an image on a Web page is a rectangular pictorial object that occupies a computer file. Images are characterized by the number of rows of pixels they contain, also called the height of an image, and the number of columns of pixels they contain which we can call the width. You can figure out the total number of pixels in an image by simply multiplying the height by the width. While you might not be familiar with creating computer graphics, most people have created a word processing document. A word processing document is just a different type of object that also occupies a file. Just as there are word processing programs to compose and modify text, image processing programs are used to work on pictures. Generally the name of a word processing document ends with a special suffix. For example, HTML files end with .html and Microsoft Word files end with .doc. Similarly, the name of a Web graphic file would usually end with either .gif or .jpg. These two names are used to label the two popular image formats for the Web—the gif format and the jpeg (jpg) format. The gif format is used to store icons, animations, or graphics with a small number of colors. Jpeg files are used to store more complex images, such as photos.

With creativity and image manipulation software you can make smaller image files and still have them look good. Such software allows you to reduce the number of rows and columns thus shrinking the image. Of course, as you make an image smaller, it naturally loses some of its resolution. In addition to simply shrinking the size of an image, the gif format allows you to reduce the number of bits used to store the color information for each pixel, a technique called "reducing the color space." For example, a gif file with only two colors requires just a single bit to represent each pixel. Since a bit can either be a 1 or a 0, each of these two values can be associated with one of the two colors in the palette. Gif files can contain 2, 4, 8, 16, 32, 64, 128, or 256 colors. You might recognize these numbers as powers of two starting with 2^1 and going to 2^8. The fewer the number of bits that are needed to store the color for each pixel, the smaller the image file. Again, there is a tradeoff since more colors generally means a more vivid image. That is where artistic creativity and judgment comes in.

One simple technique you can use to help speed the loading of a page containing images is to use two of the parameters for the <img> markup, namely height= and width=. This technique takes advantage of the fact that the text for a page generally arrives at the visitor's desktop before the images that are interspersed within that text. Lets say that somewhere in your page you have an image of a tree with 200 rows and 50 columns. Your markup might look like:

```
<img src="tree.jpg" height=200 width=50>
```

By including the height= and width= parameters, you are pre-notifying the visitor's browser of the exact size of the image that is coming. That way the browser can begin to show the text to the visitor even if the image has not arrived, since the browser can reserve the appropriate space for the image in the window. This contributes to the psychological speed of the page since the visitor has something to read even though the page has not fully loaded.

The reason that the above trick works is that the text for the page, residing in the HTML file, is the first to arrive at the visitor's computer. This leads to the general principle that if you can achieve the same effect in one of two ways: using HTML; or by using an image file; it is preferable to use HTML. Several markups allow you to modify the background color and the color of text, including <font>, <div> and the various markups associated with tables such as <table>, <tr> and <td>. If all you need to do is to present words, stick to HTML.

Another trick employed by Web page designers is to break larger images into smaller pieces. Since each piece resides in a separate file, each of these files tends to be small. The full image will still take about the same amount of time to completely arrive at the visitor's desktop, but some individual pieces will get there relatively quickly and give the visitor something to look at while the rest is on its way. Often what counts is the psychological perception of time, not what the clock says.

Fine Tuning the Artwork

It is fairly common to use an image as the anchor for a link. For example, you might have an icon of a magnifying glass as the anchor to a page that lets the visitor search your site. It is also possible to embed several links in an image. This second technique is known as an image map. There is a parameter to the <img> markup, border=0, that eliminates the blue border around a clickable image. Graphic artists often eliminate this border for artistic reasons even though it provides a clue to the visitor that they can click on the image. You must be careful, however, since Web surfers might not know that your image is clickable or how it works. Often times newcomers to the Internet are not aware that you can click on images. Unless your goal is to challenge the visitor, you need to make sure that the meaning of the icon is obvious, and that the visitor knows the image is clickable. Often pages with clickable images also contain redundant text just in case someone doesn't realize they can click on the images, or in case someone has set up their browser so that they cannot view images on a page.

The <img> markup is not the only HTML command that deals with images. Another HTML command that can be used to include images is the <body> markup. You can use a statement like:

```
<body background="filename">
```

to include the image stored in *filename* as the background for your page.

If the image is too small to fit in the window, it is **tiled,** or repeated by the browser. Tiling can be used to economize on the size of images. Suppose you want to have a star every few inches in your background. Your background image could consist of a small image containing a single star in the middle. When the image is tiled, the stars spread all over the page. Tiling is a very economical way of creating complex backgrounds that do not require much bandwidth.

A numerical scheme is used to represent color in gif images. Since any color on a computer display is a combination of the three colors—red, green and blue—any color can be described with three numbers. Each of these numbers goes from 0 to 255. The numbers 0, 0, 0 would represent pure black and 255, 255, 255 would be pure white. A color like 255, 0, 0 would be a very pure form of red.

This basic numbering plan is also used in HTML to specify background colors and the colors for text. The <body> markup includes parameters for bgcolor=, text=, link= and vlink=, each of which allows you to specify a color. Bgcolor= specifies the background color, text= specifies the color of text, link= specifies the color of a link, and vlink= specifies the color of a visited link. Note that changing the colors of links and visited links can confuse visitors. The table markups <table>, <th>, <tr> and <td> also have bgcolor= parameters, as do the <font> and <div> markups.

A slight complication in the way that all of these markups work is that HTML uses **base 16** to specify the three numbers. In base 16, the digits start at zero but keep going until 15. Here is a table of comparison between base 10 and base 16.

Base 10	Base 16	Base 10	Base 16	Base 10	Base 16
0	0	6	6	12	C
1	1	7	7	13	D
2	2	8	8	14	E
3	3	9	9	15	F
4	4	10	A	16	10
5	5	11	B		

To translate a number like 162 into base 16, you would divide it by 16. As 16 goes into 160 10 times, the first base 16 digit would be A. There are two left over, so the second base 16 digit would be 2. Thus, 162 in base 10 is A2 in base 16. While this is a bit complex, you might note that software such as Netscape Composer or Microsoft's FrontPage let you pick from a moderately sized list of options and therefore let you avoid dealing with base 16. But like many other aspects of creating pages, to achieve total control over the look of a page you must get down and dirty with the details!

Since computer images are always rectangular, **transparency** is the only way to create non-rectangular shapes for Web pages. You can convert a rectangular photograph to something that looks non-rectangular, by using an eraser or some related tool in an image processing program. The eraser can be used to change all of the pixels surrounding your subject to the color used as the background= color used on your page. This will make the image seem to be non-rectangular and float on the page. If the page background has a pattern, and you still want to create the illusion of a non-rectangular image, you need to use the transparency option of the gif standard. You can specify one of the colors in a gif file to be the transparent color. Instead of showing up on the Web page, the color will be transparent to the background behind it.

Anti-aliasing is a common print technique used to blend or smooth jagged edges. But anti-aliasing should not be used for Web images since it adds to file size and makes it more difficult to produce a transparent background for an image because of the resulting fringe or halo.

Summary

1.   Web pages are created with the Hypertext Markup Language (HTML). Using HTML involves adding embedded commands around your text that control how the browser displays that text.

2.   Markups exist to start and end a page, to embed an image, to create a link and to format words and paragraphs.

3.   Many products can be used to create HTML, including Notepad, Word, and Netscape Composer.

4.   Keep images on a Web page as small as possible.

5.   A computer screen consists of pixels.

6.   Use of transparency can make pictures more interesting.

7.   HTML has a number of markups for images and colors.

8.   HTML color specification uses base 16.

Online Activities

Visit the companion Web site at www.wiley.com/college/hofacker for chapter summaries, examples, hypertext cases, homework assignments, text material updates, research exercises, and *Wall Street Journal Interactive Edition* access.

GO TO   http://www.wiley.com/college/hofacker

References

Stern, Jim (1997) *What Makes People Click?* Indianapolis, IN: Que.

Siegel, David (1996) *Creating Killer Web Sites*, Hayden Books.

Ware, Scott, Michael Tracy, Louis Slothouber and Robert Baker (1997) *Professional Web Site Optimization*, Wrox Press.

Weinman, Lynda (1997). *Preparing Web Graphics*. Indianapolis, IN: New Riders Publishing.

Weinman, Lynda (1998) <FONT> Talk, *Web Techniques,* 3 (6), 18-21.

WEB COMMUNICATIONS STRATEGY

1. Evaluate how a firm's Internet presence relates to its overall communication objectives.
2. Discuss the difference between a flat ad and a marketing site.
3. Learn the importance of establishing relationships with consumers.

Web Site Communication Goals

In this chapter we discuss using a World Wide Web home page to communicate with consumers about a company's products or services. Just a few years ago, it was considered leading edge to have any kind of promotional Web site at all. Today companies wrestle with the problems of what works and what doesn't, and how to keep the Web site fresh after the initial accomplishment of putting it up has passed.

Despite differences between the Internet and other media, planning your advertising on the Internet has many elements in common with other forms of advertising. As with any ad campaign, your Web objectives should be integrated into your overall marketing communications goals. These goals vary from firm to firm depending on the nature of the product, and where it is in the **product life cycle**. For brand new products, there is often little competition and the goal may be to simply get the word out about the benefits of this new offering. For more mature products, we find competition heating up and companies using various communications channels to differentiate their product from the many competitors', or to suggest new uses for an old product. The type of message we send will also depend on the nature of the consumer decision. When the consumer buys our category of product in a routine or mundane manner we would generally use a more image oriented, feeling approach. On the other hand, when the consumer faces a complex buying decision, we would tend to alter the message to be much more thinking oriented.

Just as with traditional media, you must also contemplate exactly who your target audience is. How old are they? Where do they live? Are they mostly male or mostly female? Are they worried about this product category? What sorts of attitudes and opinions do they hold? What do they enjoy doing or reading about? Once you have studied your target audience, most often you will then pick from among the following communications goals:

Consumer awareness. You want the consumer to know who you are and what you offer. The consumer may not be knowledgeable about the benefits you offer or why your services are better than your competitors'.

Image. Your advertising objective might be to convey a certain image. In this case the goal is to impart some emotion, or to associate yourself with certain positive feelings. In this case you are using your Web site to facilitate a favorable consumer attitude.

Mindshare. An established firm might wish to keep its name and brands in the public eye. When the consumer goes to buy, you want them to think of you.

Trial. A new firm or a firm with a new product or service might want to get the consumer to try it.

Accelerating repurchase. Profitability for consumer goods bought in supermarkets like frozen food, or a service like a haircut, can be increased if the consumer can be persuaded to buy more often. In this case, the goal is to change the consumer's behavior.

Once your communications goal is determined, it is important to think through your online budget. The budget should be coordinated in a logical way to the financial goals for the communication. Ultimately the bottom line for a communications Web site is the bottom line. What this means is that the site should pay for itself in terms of long term increased sales, market share, or profit. It is important to realize however that measuring the impact of a well executed Web site on these objective financial measures is devilishly tricky. At this time there are no good economic studies of the return on investment for communications Web sites, nor at the moment are there any estimates for the **Web communication elasticity of sales**. In other words, no one can say with much assurance how much your sales will increase for each dollar, or Euro, or Yen you invest in your Web site. For the time being, we must rely on simple observation of what is going on in the market and on managerial intuition. One thing is certain, however. You need to have a plan and budgetary support in place to react to consumer email. Unlike TV and other mass media, the consumer will talk back to you! An informal check done by *The New York Times* showed that numerous companies that invite email queries take weeks or more to reply to these messages. Worse yet, many companies never respond at all! Every day you wait to reply to email reduces the probability that the exchange with the consumer will lead to a sale. With the Internet, it is important to remember that you are not just talking at the consumer, you are trying to enter into a relationship with them. Of course, relationships generally don't work out when one party ignores the communication of the other! We now turn to some further explanation of the nature of this relationship.

Establishing Online Relationships

The first thing to keep in mind is that a Web site used to promote or advertise a business is unlike a traditional ad in that it does not intrude. To briefly review some concepts presented in Chapter 2, we note that the Web is mostly a **pull** medium rather than a **push** medium. In this respect, the Yellow Pages make a better analogy to a Web site than an ad in a magazine or on TV. Also, unlike the case with mass media, your audience is by no means captive. The essence of the Internet is that it is user driven, and not controlled by the Web site owner. A second analogy for the net would be to the phone system. Users can and will leave your site at any time, that is unless you give them something interesting or useful to look at. And they can talk back, and they will. In fact, the ability of the consumer to talk to you and to talk to each other is not something to fear. On the contrary, it is one of the Internet's greatest strengths as a marketing medium. Successful firms will learn to welcome the prospect of the active net consumer, and will find themselves able to benefit from the energy of the consumer.

Let us now distinguish between two classes of promotional or communication Web sites: the **flat ad** and the **marketing site**. A flat ad contains the kind of information found on a brochure: the company's toll-free number, its products or services, its email address, and perhaps where its headquarters are located. It is designed to respond to customer-initiated online communication. A flat ad is fairly simple to set up, and so many companies initiate their online presence this way. Consumers can use these simple Web sites to request a sales call, to learn the toll free phone number for your firm, to find out the location of the nearest dealer, or some basic facts about your offerings, or to ask a question.

Admittedly, these days a flat ad is considered a fairly primitive level of online presence. Often such sites are jokingly referred to as "brochureware", or "shovelware." Yet even here, a simple site or a straightforward page of information can be quite powerful, especially when used in conjunction with other media. A flat ad can serve to supplement the information presented in a more expensive mass medium ad or in a mail out. The URL of the site, or a sub-URL, can appear in an outdoor or print ad, or at the end of a radio or television commercial. Consumers can then use the Web to retrieve far more information than you could ever include in a broadcast or print ad, or even in a direct mail piece.

Now we turn to the marketing site, which is more like a product in and of itself, than an actual advertisement. Compared to a flat ad, which is like a factual brochure, a marketing site is more like an engaging magazine. It is designed to pull consumers to the site, perhaps in conjunction with banners or links. Rather than being focused purely on information, it is marketing- and action-oriented, designed to move the consumer closer to a sale in the short and middle terms. The long-term goal of a marketing site is to establish a relationship with the consumer. A marketing site uses Internet services for interaction with the consumer and perhaps to let consumers interact with each other. We discuss these interactions next.

Internet marketing is often referred to as **interactive marketing**. The sequence of clicks and typed in responses made by a consumer during interaction with the site can be stored. When that individual returns, the software behind the site can retrieve the previous interaction and customize the new visit. In this sense, the interactive nature of the Internet bears some resemblance to the technique of a skilled salesperson. A good site can put a human—or almost human—face on the conversation between the site and the consumer. In this sense, interactivity goes well beyond what you can do with mass media advertising. The site creates a two-way conversation with consumers, a conversation that is satisfying for both parties. Do this for many consumers, and you have what is known as **mass customization**. Networked computers can offer a personal exchange with a large audience without an impossibly huge cost burden.

In truth, it is far cheaper to retain a previous customer than to get a new one. The benefit of the relationship between the firm and the customer has led many service companies to create "Frequent Flyer Points" or other symbolic embodiments of the relationship. Such plans are designed to enhance consumer loyalty. Analogously, some sites have initiated "Frequent Visitor Points." Beyond loyalty, the motivation of such schemes is to enter into an informational exchange with the consumer. Retaining the customer becomes all the more easier the more you know about that person. But why should the customer be willing to give you information? What do they get out of the exchange? From the consumer's point of view, the relationship can serve to reduce purchase risks. But as we further contemplate the nature of choice we find that a firm can actually do it's consumers a favor by knowing them well enough to reduce their choices.

Most of us have it in our minds that lots of choice is always good. We can buy any of 51 different flavors of ice cream, and we can put all kinds of toppings on our pizza. But for a moment, consider what goes on when you go to have your hair cut or styled. It is true that we can have our hair done in any one of hundreds of styles. But most of the time we don't really want to go through all the work it takes to choose hairstyles; what we want is to get our hair done the way we like it. Why do you go to the same hairstylist or barber? One reason is that her or she knows how you like your hair. You don't have to explain each time how you want it. You don't have to go through a couple of cuts to get it right. Your stylist knows how to do it the way you like it. In short, you have a relationship.

A relationship can act to reduce choice for the consumer and thereby make purchasing decisions easier. By opting into a relationship, the consumer can simplify the cognitive work and mental effort required for buying. This is all the more true as consumers feel increasing time pressures in their lives. The benefits of choice reduction are especially prevalent when the product category is complex, where there is some risk associated with purchase, or if it is time-consuming or difficult for the consumer to specify his or her preferences. In these situations, when the company remembers the consumer's preferences it reduces the consumer's burden even more.

Even if an immediate sale is not made during an interactive session, it may be that the firm can come away with something valuable by learning about the customer; how loyal he or she is, perhaps garner an email or postal address or even something about their attitudes, interests, or opinions. The network facilitated communication between the customer and the firm, unlike the unidirectional informational flow that occurs in the mass media, produces a sense of reciprocity and equality between the firm and the customer. And information so learned in these interactive sessions can be kept in a profile database and used to generate leads or to better match offers with customers, further customizing the relationship, a technique called **database marketing**.

Another powerful aspect of the Web is that it can be used to let customers communicate among themselves. The sponsoring promotional site can donate a **virtual space** where this conversation can take place. The space is virtual in the sense that it is created with computer processing and disk-drive storage. For example, Stolichnya Vodka's site provides a place for customers to trade recipes for their favorite vodka drinks, and the Saturn site sponsors space for owners to post pictures of themselves with their Saturn cars. Another example can be found at the Medistore, which is targeted at people with chronic medical problems. This site offers support groups for various kinds of illness at their site. Visitors can post questions, advice, or commiseration with their fellow patients.

These interest-oriented groupings of customers are an example of what is called a **virtual community**. In a virtual community, the focus of the conversation is on the customer and on the customer's needs and interests; information that firms usually have to spend a lot of money on to track. In addition, the community can add value for you in ways that the company could not hope to do by itself. The communication in the community becomes valuable content offered on the site. In effect, your customers become your helpers. All of these activities on the Web site can help to build a sense of commitment and trust toward the company. The goal is to partner with customers, to solicit questions, input, and dialogue, and to create intimacy of a sort.

Allowing virtual communities to flower can go against the grain of a corporate culture steeped in the notion that the company has the sole right to control its own marketing communications. If customers can say what they want, they can criticize the product, right? One important lesson of the Internet is that consumers already have the power to talk amongst themselves and criticize what they see as company mistakes. Intel, among others, learned this lesson in the middle 1990's when one of its chips exhibited what the company thought of as a trivial, unimportant bug. Consumers on Usenet thought otherwise. Today, the net savvy firm neither tries to ignore Internet conversation nor squelch it. Instead, by hosting and facilitating the conversation the firm has easy access to an early warning system for problems. And in cases of criticism, how a company reacts to the problem is usually more important than the details of the problem itself. Criticism is an opportunity for a company to show it is worthy of its side of the relationship.

The issue of control was faced by Nintendo of Canada when they first went to create their own marketing site on the Internet. They discovered over 70 "Nintendo" Web sites already in existence, all having been created by hobbyists and other game enthusiasts. The company was faced with the decision as to whether they should try to attack these sites through the courts. Instead, they went in the opposite direction and joined with the sites, a process often called co-option. They gave the Web masters of these sites inside information, allowing these opinion leaders to see all of their press releases and letting them have access to company software game developers. Instead of angering 70 of their most influential customers, they leveraged the enthusiasm in the market to benefit everyone.

The possibilities for facilitating the relationships on the net are truly legion. Information presented as edutainment can lead to increased consumption, as might be the case with recipes or tips for use. Pages can be set up to discuss uses, features, specifications, add-ons, fixes, or corrections. Some other techniques that leverage the Internet's interactive nature are contests, coupons, prizes, search capabilities, electronic newsletters, or feedback forms. A sports clothing company could let the visitor create his or her own team and enter into competition with others. A financial services company could create discussion areas for investors to talk about investment strategy. One clever example was created by the Canadian brewer Molson, who sponsors a mini camera that gets passed around on a button in various night spots. These types of activities extend the perceived value of the purchase and increase consumer involvement with the brand.

Summary

1. An Internet site can help with a company's consumer awareness, image, mindshare, trial, or repurchase goals.

2. Relationships benefit the consumer by reducing risk and the cognitive work load associated with choice.

3. A Web site can remember things about the customers' likes, needs, and preferences. It can then customize future interaction to enhance the consumers' experiences.

4. A Web site is more like a conversation than a commercial.

5. Providing a space for customers to talk among themselves can add value to the site.

6. There are many creative ways to use interactivity to engage the consumer and enhance the relationship.

Online Activities

Visit the companion Web site at www.wiley.com/college/hofacker for chapter summaries, examples, hypertext cases, homework assignments, text material updates, research exercises, and *Wall Street Journal Interactive Edition* access.

GO TO	http://www.wiley.com/college/hofacker

THE WALL STREET JOURNAL.

References

Armstrong, Arthur and John Hagen (1996) The Real Value of Online Communities, *Harvard Business Review*, (May-June), 134-141.

Bejou, David (1997) Relationship Marketing: Evolution, Present State and Future, *Psychology and Marketing*, 14 (8), 727-736.

Blattberg, Robert C. and John Deighton (1991) Interactive Marketing: Exploiting the Age of Addressability, *Sloan Management Review*, 33 (Fall), 5-14.

Duncan, Tom and Sandra E. Moriarty (1998) A Communication-Based Model for Managing Relationships, *Journal of Marketing*, 62 (April), 1-13.

Ghose, Sanjoy and Wenyu Dou (1998) Interactive Functions and their Impacts on the Appeal of Internet Presence Sites, *Journal of Advertising Research*, 38 (March/April), 29-43.

Hagel, John III and Arthur G. Armstrong, *Net Gain: Expanding Markets through Virtual Communities*. Boston: Harvard Business School Press, 1997.

Kotler, Phillip (1989) From Mass Marketing to Mass Customization, *Planning Review*, 47 (September/October), 10-13.

Loebbecke, C., P. Powell and S. Trilling (1998) Investigating the Worth of Internet Advertising, *International Journal of Information Management*, 18 (June), 181-193.

McKenna, Regis (1995) Real-Time Marketing, *Harvard Business Review*, 73 (July/August), 87-95.

Peters, Linda (1998) The New Interactive Media: One-to-One, but Who to Whom? *Marketing Intelligence & Planning*, 16 (1), 22-30.

Peppers, Don and Martha Rogers, *Enterprise One to One: Tools for Competing in the Interactive Age*. New York: Doubleday, 1997.

Raman, Niranjan V. and John D. Leckenby (1998) Factors Affecting Consumers' "Webad" Visits, *European Journal of Marketing,* 32 (7/8), 737-748.

Schwartz, Evan I. (1997) *Webonomics*. Broadway Books.

Shaver, Dick (1996) *The Next Step in Database Marketing: Consumer Guided Marketing*, New York: Wiley.

Sheth, Jagdish N. and Atul Parvatiyar (1991) Relationship Marketing in Consumer Markets: Antecedents and Consequences, *Journal of the Academy of Marketing Science*, Fall, 255-271.

HUMAN INFORMATION PROCESSING OF WEB SITES

LEARNING OBJECTIVES

1. Understand the weaknesses brought to the Web by the human information processor and how it impacts the way a site should look.
2. Learn the stages of informational flow within the mind of the consumer.

When a consumer looks at a Web page or a banner, the information that is presented there is processed by the human mind in several separate stages. Each of these stages is like a gateway. If the information does not make it past a stage, it is lost and the consumer has not been impacted by it. A site will only be effective in meeting your marketing goals if the information presented on it survives to the last stage—when the consumer has stored this information in his mind and can retrieve it again. The stages presented below are quite important for communications sites, but they are also relevant in creating effective ad banners, and selling sites and content sites. The stages are 1) exposure, 2) attention, 3) comprehension and perception, 4) yielding and acceptance, and 5) retention.

Exposure

Despite claims of "subliminal perception," not much happens unless the consumer is exposed to something long enough for him to absorb what he has seen. Quickly disappearing messages or flickering words that cannot be easily read will not be processed by the visitor and cannot affect them in any significant way. Many Web visitors do not use the scroll bar on the right-hand side of their browser to look at the lower parts of a page. The implication is that if you want a certain piece of information to be exposed to the consumer, it needs to appear in the top part of the page. It is even less likely that a visitor will use the horizontal scroll bar, so try to avoid placing important information off the screen to the right. At least if the key information is in front of the consumer, you have a chance for it to make it to the next stage, which is attention.

Attention

Attention is one of the main bottlenecks of the human mind. Given enough time, we can memorize and store in our minds millions of facts, but we can only pay attention to a small number of them at a time.

A large number of factors have an influence over what attracts our attention, and these factors constantly shift and change. To some extent our attention is under our control. We choose what to notice and look at depending on our motivation. In other words, if a consumer is looking to buy a new recreational vehicle and a banner advertisement for Winnebago appears on the screen, he will be more likely to stop looking at the page he is on and focus for a time on that ad. Attention is also dependent on our expectations. There are many times when we fail to notice something because we did not expect to see it. But the opposite phenomenon can occur also. Sometimes we notice something we usually wouldn't when it is presented in a novel or different way. Thus the rules for attracting attention should not be oversimplified. A visitor might not notice an ad on a page where an ad is expected, especially if it blends in with the rest of the site, but a banner ad that appears where there hadn't been one before might be noticed right away.

Attention is impacted by various physical factors in the visual field including movement, size, and intensity. It is much easier to notice things that move, bigger objects, more intense or more attractive stimuli, and bright or loud things. Take care to use this knowledge with caution and moderation. If we make everything on a page move, nothing on the page will stand out and grab attention. Using these physical properties should be reserved for the most important parts of a page, or for the link or image that you really want people to focus on.

This warning leads to another principle: Contrast and novelty command attention. When things are new or when they change we tend to notice. You may have heard the story about the two roommates who moved into an apartment next to a noisy factory. After a few days they got used to the noise, and it didn't bother them at all. Then once in the middle of the night, they both woke up at the same time, jumped out of bed and ran out into the hallway. "What was that sound?" they shouted to each other. They listened for a while and realized that there was no sound. What had awakened them was that the factory had suddenly gone quiet. We notice change in our environment—it attracts attention. If most of a Web page is red and a small part of the page is green, we will tend to notice the green sections. If your entire page is in bold font, and just a key message is in normal text, the visitor may well attend to the normal text. The contrast or the changed part of the message is the part that people are most likely to pay attention to first.

You can use these principles to help visitors as they skim your page. You can use some type of highlighting, whether it is through bold text, or a color change, or a different font, to help them quickly scan for the most important offerings. If the visitor chooses to allocate enough time on attending to these important elements, there is a chance they will be comprehended, a topic that is covered next.

Comprehension and Perception

The terms "comprehension" and "perception" refer to the process that occurs when an exposed element in the physical environment is attended to, and contact is made between that element and information about it stored in long-term memory. To illustrate the idea, we will cover two examples, one visual and one verbal. For the visual example, say you have a picture on your Web site of a man sitting on a donkey and holding a knight's lance, with the man preparing to attack a windmill. If the visitors pay attention to this for enough time, the information contained in the picture will connect with the stored information in their mind about Don Quixote, impossible dreams, and tilting at windmills. We would then say that the image was comprehended or perceived. For a verbal example, suppose you used the phrase, "It would be like rearranging the chairs on deck of the *Titanic*." What does this mean? If the visitor to the site shares the same culture that you do, the visitor would know that the *Titanic* was a large ship that sank, and that moving deck chairs around would have been busy work that wouldn't have helped save the ship at all. The users' store of cultural and historical information allows the phrase to be comprehended. Only through familiarity with the original information can the allusion be understood. When the image of the *Titanic*, or of the windmill, connects with previously stored information on this topic, we can say that the image has been perceived or comprehended.

The act of comprehension is what provides a context for the page element. There are many types of such stored information. There are facts, meanings and definitions, associations, recollections, icons, and more. One very important type of stored representations is called a *schema*. A schema is an organized collection of information about the world with many embedded parts. For example, you might have a schema stored in your memory about how a business lunch is supposed to work. There is a certain sequence of events, a certain way to dress, and a certain way to behave. If page elements included aspects of a business lunch, these elements would make contact with the schema for a business lunch and be understood in that context.

Stored information can allow a Web site to be designed as an extended metaphor. A site might look like an old-time drive-in movie theater, and clicking on the screen or on the cars would do something consistent with most people's schema of what drive-ins were all about. But as drive-ins get increasingly rare, younger people might not know what they are and the metaphor will fail to be effective. What people have stored in their minds and what they are able to comprehend is dependent on culture and what they are taught in their society. You might have noticed that the controls for some types of software looks like the controls for a CD player or a tape player. The metaphor works to create easy understanding because today most users are familiar with CD players or tape players.

You can frustrate visitors if you go against what they already know. Computer software engineers speak of using a **mode razor**. If each mode of operation of a program has different rules, this can make software difficult to learn or use. The razor concept implies that you should shave away as many modes as possible. This philosophy means that the "rules" for your Web pages should not change. Once someone learns the rules, they can easily perceive the way the whole site works.

Unfortunately, **frames** are a type of Web design philosophy that creates a whole new mode with its own rules. You can recognize a site using frames when you see more than one scroll bar, or when the URL in the location window of your browser does not change even when you click on various links. Frames change the appearance and the very definition of what constitutes a "Web site." Frames also change the way the back arrow works, they modify what happens when you click on a link, and they modify the way that URLs work. The most basic and fundamental unit of navigation on the Web is the "page." Frames modify this. In addition, they make it impossible for a visitor to bookmark a page within a site, and they further make it inconvenient and difficult to communicate the address of a page within a site. In short, use of frames may be a bad idea since it is likely to utterly confuse a large number of site visitors—it violates most people's schema of what a Web site is and does. It is possible to divide the screen into pieces using HTML tables instead—it requires more complex programming, but it will not confuse your customers.

Pursuing the mode razor concept, note that it implies we should keep lists of menu choices that appear on different pages in the same order every time they appear. You could consistently use a particular color scheme for different parts of a site to help keep people oriented. You might pick red borders for the pages that describe one product category and pick blue borders for another product category. You could do something similar with other graphical or stylistic elements. Visual elements can also be used to emphasize the overall site format, to partition the screen and categorize information, or to draw attention to important links, specials, or timely information. You might have a left-hand runner with a red background on every page that provides a main menu for the site, and a blank with a search button. Or you could use the upper right-hand part of the screen for a series of links labeled up, back, and top. The font for these links could always be the same, and this font would be different than the one you use for the main body of each page. The special of the day could always be in the upper left-hand corner in large type. All of these examples rely on the simple notion that you shouldn't change the rules for your site haphazardly.

As described above in the section on exposure, it is a general rule that the most important options on a page should fit on a single screen because many users will not use the horizontal and vertical scroll bars. Of course, this means a screen of 640 by 480 pixels, which is today's lowest common denominator of computer monitor. If there is too much information to fit on one screen, you can increase menu depth by creating sub-menus. But be careful—as sub-menus go deeper and deeper visitors could get lost or confused about where they are. It is incumbent on the site designer to make sure there are cues for easy navigation no matter how deeply into the site the consumer has traveled. One rule of thumb is to try to keep everything on the site within a small number of clicks, perhaps three to five, of everything else on the site.

Computer users fare better when you give them feedback. If you ask them to do something unusual, make sure they can figure out whether they have successfully done so. This is especially important when users are filling out forms of various kinds. But it can be as simple as "graying out" the button for the current page so that they know not to press the button to take them to a page they are already looking at. A Web page must do double duty—it must present the information or content that is on the page and it must help the visitor navigate through your **information space**: the collection of knowledge on your site and the ways it is interconnected. To navigate effectively, the user needs some intuition, she needs to create some kind of a mental representation of your site so that she knows how the various pages relate or connect to each to other. You need to help her create a schema for the site, perhaps with a site map. The map can be used to indicate how the various pages relate to and fit into the rest of the site. In the case of a simple flat ad, one approach is to put a brand or company logo in the same spot, perhaps the upper left, of every page. Clicking on this takes your users back to your home page. In the case of a complex site the task becomes more difficult for both the Web designer as well as the consumer trying to find something.

Sometimes the most obvious way to structure an information space is not the best way. Many companies organize their Web site to mirror the administration of the company. While this might make sense to employees of the firm, consumers will likely not have any background information about how your company is structured. It is far better to organize the information in a way that would be logical to the visitor.

Yielding and Acceptance

The information that you present may or may not be accepted by the consumer. If the site or banner is set up to provide factual information, compared to an emotional or image-based appeal, you might provide supporting arguments for what you want the visitor to do. The arguments that you make might provoke counter-arguments in the mind of the visitor, however. But if you have done marketing research, you may be able to anticipate the nature of these counter-arguments and preemptively combat them in your appeal. Another tactic is to derogate the source of possible counter-arguments. If a competing brand is the source of arguments, you can attack their credibility and motivation.

Retention

Promotional sites exist to enhance the sales of a product or service. But will the information presented on the site be remembered when it comes time for the consumer to purchase? Will the consumer be able to find your site again later? The answers to these questions depend on what is stored in and retrievable from the memory systems of your consumers. Generally speaking, it is easier to remember information from a site that is well organized. Therefore, the factors listed above that make a site easier to comprehend will also make it easier for the consumer to remember what you present. On the other hand, if the site appears as just a jumble of unrelated pages, the consumer will be about as successful in retrieving information from his own mind as he was from the site, which is to say, not very successful at all. A good organization provides a reliable set of memory "hooks" that the mind can use to "hang the information on."

People more easily recall concrete information than abstract information. Anything that you can do to create a concrete visual image related to the product will help the consumer better retain information from the site.

With the proliferation of sites, it is increasingly difficult for consumers to remember where they saw something on the Web. In fact, bookmark management is so difficult with today's browsers that after-market software products are available solely to help people with that task. In order to get your site bookmarked, you should try to create a landmark that the consumer will see as a useful resource of some kind. And since the HTML <title> markup is used by browsers such as Netscape Navigator or Internet Explorer to serve as a label for a bookmark entry, give careful thought to what should appear within the title markup. When visitors are looking over their bookmarks, you want them to be able to recognize your entry and be compelled by the title to return.

Summary

1. Design of a Web site should take into account the five stages information goes through in the mind: exposure, attention, comprehension and perception, yielding and acceptance, and retention.
2. Artistic elements, page copy, and the way the site is structured should take into account that information must pass through all five stages to impact consumer behavior.
3. Much thought should be given to the design of your information space, and the means by which consumers will be able to navigate through it.

Online Activities

Visit the companion Web site at www.wiley.com/college/hofacker for chapter summaries, examples, hypertext cases, homework assignments, text material updates, research exercises, and *Wall Street Journal Interactive Edition* access.

GO TO http://www.wiley.com/college/hofacker

WSj .com THE WALL STREET JOURNAL.

References

Burton, J. K., D. M. Moore and G. A. Holmes (1995) Hypermedia Concepts and Research: An Overview, *Computers in Human Behavior*, 11 (3), 345-369.

Eighmey, John (1997) Profiling User Responses to Commercial Web Sites, *Journal of Advertising Research*, 37 (May-June), 59-66.

Scholten, Marc (1996) Lost and Found: The Information-Processing Model of Advertising Effectiveness, *Journal of Business Research* 37 (2), 97-104.

What a Web Site Should Look Like

LEARNING OBJECTIVES

1. Understand the difference between the three ways of setting up a home page: front door, banner and menu, and runner and main page.
2. Learn such artistic principles as perceptual wholeness, balance, movement, color and contrast.

The purpose of this chapter is to consider the details of designing a company's home page—the visual layout or format of the page, or how it looks. These details are a mix of aesthetics and cold analysis. Despite the many obvious differences between a Web page and a magazine page, we can borrow many rules from print media. The Web and a printed page are similar in that both are comprised of two-dimensional surfaces. While ads on a Web page might be animated, the page structure or layout is generally static. But there is much to this topic that makes it more of an art than a science. Many times, really good ads are good because they break the rules. But it is difficult to effectively break a rule if you don't know the rule to begin with!

There is a very common pitfall that strikes many home pages. Most companies employing Web page designers buy top-notch equipment, but these designers might forget about viewers who don't have such luxuries. It is easy to fall into the trap of thinking that everybody has a speedy network connection, an ultra-fast new computer, and a huge monitor. As has been reiterated often in this book, with computer-mediated communication the locus of control tends to be local. And the type of computer and the size of the monitor impose as much control as anything over how the page will look to the consumer. It is essential to test all pages on many types of computers and monitors, including television screens. Images come out brighter on Macs and darker on PCs. Pages look entirely different on Web TV.

There are three classic ways to set up a home page. These are the "front door" metaphor, the "banner and menu" style, and the "runner and main page" format.

Front Door

In this method the initial page, sometimes called a **splash page**, is nothing more than an invitation to enter the real site. Often this method is executed using some sort of metaphor that lets the art illustrate the primary message. A headline may be used on the splash page that integrates with the visual elements or creates some kind of visual pun.

For example, the front page for a restaurant featuring home style cooking might look like the front porch of a country shack. The headline, designed to resemble pieces of a carved tree, might beckon viewers to "come on in" with some folksy language. The user would enter the site by clicking on the picture of the rustic wooden door.

Artists use various components to create a **perceptual whole**. That is, the images on a Web page must be built from related pieces. The visual elements must be chosen to blend somehow into a single, overall impression. You wouldn't try to mix and match the front door described above with modern fonts. All elements in the site design need to share a common theme. Successfully executing such a design requires skill and a lot of knowledge about our culture and about how consumers will perceive things.

Banner and Menu

The 1980s text-oriented computer menus inspire the basic "banner and menu" setup with a banner image at the top of the page followed by a menu. The banner may be clickable, offering shortcuts for the visitor to get to sub-pages. The company logo can be worked into the banner. There may also be a text headline either at the top of the page or integrated into the banner. Depending on the communications goal of the site, the headline should either be action- or awareness-oriented. Subheadlines can be used to amplify the orientation of the headline, or perhaps used to allow a shorter headline. A menu of sub-pages appears below the banner. Often this menu appears in the form of a bulleted list.

The banner headline, the subheadlines, and the menu copy use a set of related **typefaces**, usually differing in size. Typefaces are categorized by whether they have **serifs** or not. Serifs are thin cross lines that adorn letters. "Roman," one popular typeface, has broad and thin strokes with serifs. You can control the typeface for a Web page using the <font> markup. You can also control the **weight**, or degree of blackness from light to bold, of the typeface using the <b> markup. A good choice of a typeface can contribute to the mood you are trying to create or the style you are trying to effect.

Traditionally, the size of typeface is measured in points, with 72 points to the inch. On the Web, each user can control the size of fonts on their own screen, making control of the appearance of the page problematic. You do have some control over this factor using either the size parameter of the <font> markup, or the headline (<h1>, for example) markup.

Artists know that sometimes the white space around objects can be as important as the objects themselves. Blank space can be used to organize, to highlight, and to separate. Your menus should have a consistency in the way that they use the space on the screen, with an elegance to how everything is spaced and a rhythm to the way that the pages relate to each other. It is important to decide what you want to have in the foreground and what you want to keep in the background. Some sites have complex and noisy backgrounds which distract from the important information you really want in the foreground.

Runner and Main Page

Here the screen is divided into two sections. There is a narrow section, usually on the left, that contains a site menu or some kind of navigation bar. The main section is used to present various data including the corporate logo and other link choices. Generally the narrow section is repeated on each of the individual pages that make up the site.

An important principle of art is that a visual display needs to be balanced. If you were to draw a vertical line down the center of the page, the elements on the left and right of the line should have equal "weight." Since the runner and main page format is quite asymmetrical, it can take some creativity to achieve balance with this type of format.

Some Rules to Keep in Mind

A good page designer can create a sense of movement without employing gratuitous blinking, animation, or scrolling. You do this by drawing the eye in a certain direction. Our gaze tends to move toward larger and brighter objects. Also, we often follow arrows or pointing, or even the gaze of a person in the ad.

You should use animation with extreme caution. The chances are these elements will detract from rather than add to the communications goal for the site. Motion is a strong attention grabber—so use it only to grab attention. If you have text that you want the visitor to read, focused attention will be more difficult and less enjoyable with movement going on in that visitor's peripheral vision.

When used appropriately, color can attract attention. The human information processor is well attuned to distinctions or differences; these attract attention also. You should avoid using the standard linking colors, like blue and purple, for text.

HTML Sidebar

It is easy to create a left-hand runner on a page with the background= parameter of the <body> markup. Use an image program to create a wide but short strip. The best method is to create a strip 1024 pixels or more wide and only one pixel high. If you want the runner to be 80 pixels wide, simply make the first 80 pixels of the strip a different color. The browser will tile the strip causing it to be horizontally repeated until it fills the page.

It can be maddeningly difficult to get things to line up on a Web page. Compounding the problem is the fact that your visitors use different-sized windows on different-sized computer monitors. One trick you can use to help align objects and text is to create a single-pixel image. This image can be either transparent or the same color as the background for the page. You can use the image as a shim or as filler between objects. To change the size of the filler, you can employ the height= and width= parameters of the <img> markup.

Tables are also helpful for achieving alignment. The <table> and <td> markups have height= and width= parameters that can be specified in terms the number of pixels you want to use or in terms of the percentage of the browser window you want to take up. In addition, the cellpadding= parameter of the <table> markup can be used to create uniformly sized table cells.

You will confuse visitors into clicking on text that uses these colors. Conversely, it is not a good idea to pick nonstandard colors to use for linking. People may not know that a link is clickable unless it is highlighted in blue. Visitors also keep track of where they have been in your site, which allows them to build a mental model of your information space, by noting which links have turned from blue to purple. This change lets them keep track of the pages they have already visited.

Color can also be used to help the visitor understand how a site is structured. For example, a different color can be chosen as the theme color, for images or perhaps the background, for each of the subsections of a site.

Black makes a great background color for computer screens. Using a black background brings out foreground colors and allows the eye to see a wider variety of subtle differences. Under any circumstances, make sure there is sufficient contrast between the page background and each color of text you use.

Summary

1. There are three main ways to set up a home page. The front door method uses an initial page that is set up solely to invite consumers into the real site. The banner and menu approach includes a headline or logo followed by a bulleted list. The third approach is to create a runner on one side of the screen containing navigational aides to be used with the entire site.

2. You can use balance, color, contrast, and movement to make a site look appealing.

Online Activities

Visit the companion Web site at www.wiley.com/college/hofacker for chapter summaries, examples, hypertext cases, homework assignments, text material updates, research exercises, and *Wall Street Journal Interactive Edition* access.

GO TO http://www.wiley.com/college/hofacker

References

Baeker, Ronald M., Jonathan Grudin, William Buzton and Saul Greenberg (1995) *Readings in Human-Computer Interaction*, Second Edition, Morgan Kaufmann

Chamblee, Robert and Dennis M. Sandler (1992) Business to Business Advertising: Which Layout Style Works Best? *Journal of Advertising Research*, 32 (November/December), 39-46.

Chen, C., & Rada, R. (1996). Interacting With Hypertext: A Meta-Analysis of Experimental Studies. *Human-Computer Interaction,* 11 (2), 125-156.

Davis, Fred D. (1993) User Acceptance of Information Technology: System Characteristics, User Perceptions, and Behavioral Impacts, *International Journal of Man-Machine Studies*, 38, 982-1003.

Dholakia, Utpal M. and Lopo L. Rego (1998) What Makes Commercial Web Pages Popular? An Empirical Investigation of Web Page Effectiveness,

Drèze, Xavier and Fred Zufryden (1997) Testing Web Site Design and Promotional Content, *Journal of Advertising Research*, 37, (March-April), 77-91.

Edwards, D. M., & Hardman, L. (1989). 'Lost in Hyperspace': Cognitive Mapping and Navigation in a Hypertext Environment. In R. McAleese (Ed.), *Hypertext: Theory into Practice* Norwood, New Jersey: Ablex.

Kleinmuntz, Don N. and David A. Schkade (1993) Information Displays and Decision Processes, *Psychological Science*, 4 (July), 221-227.

Landauer, Tom (1995) *The Trouble With Computers: Usefulness, Usability and Productivity*. Cambridge, MA: MIT Press.

Palmer, Jonathan W. and David Griffith (1998) An Emerging Web Site Design Model for Marketing," *Communications of the ACM*, 41 (March), 44-51

Morris, Mary E. and Randy J. Hinrichs (1996*) Web Page Design: A Different Multimedia*. Mountain View, CA: Sunsoft Press.

Palmer, Jonathan W. (1997) Electronic Commerce in Retailing: Differences Across Retailing Formats, *The Information Society*, 13 (Winter), 97-108.

Palmer, Jonathan W. and David Griffith (1998) An Emerging Web Site Design Model for Marketing, *Communications of the ACM*, 41 (March), 44-51.

Posner, Michael I. And S. E. Peterson (1990) The Attention System of the Human Brain, *Annual Review of Neuroscience*, 13, 25-42.

Schindler, Pamela S. (1986) Color and Contrast in Magazine Advertising, *Psychology and Marketing*, 3 (Summer), 69-78.

Simpson, A., and C. McKnight (1990). Navigation in Hypertext: Structural Cues and Mental Maps. In R. McAleese and C. Green (Eds.), *Hypertext: State of the Art* Oxford, England: Intellect.

Taylor, S. and P.A. Todd (1995) Understanding Information Technology Usage: A Test of Competing Models, *Information Systems Research*, 6, 144-176.

Toub, Steve (1999) How to Design a Table of Contents, *Web Techniques*, 4 (2), 16-21.

Chapter 9

WEB SITE COPY

LEARNING OBJECTIVES

1. Understand the differences between copy in broadcast media and the Internet medium.
2. Understand how physical properties of computers and monitors differ from paper affect your presentation.
3. Learn why Web sites should be modularized and written in an inverted pyramid style.

Advertisers use the word **copy** to refer to the words and text appearing in an ad. The World Wide Web has its own style of copy, just like billboards, magazines, television, and radio have their own language and conventions. The difference between these older media and the Internet is that the user is in charge on the Web, and being in charge is different than being broadcast to. Hard sell, clichés, and hyperbole work far better on TV than on the Internet. Web surfers want to be entertained or informed. Your Web pages should help them, not talk down to them. Treat visitors to your site like adults.

Viewers will snicker, roll their eyes, and bypass pages with copy like "the absolute best ever," "world's greatest," or "you must buy this." Instead, you should focus on how your product or service can help the visitor and on what the Web site has to offer in terms of entertainment or help. One very basic and important rule is to eliminate all typos on your pages. Bad grammar or misspellings make you or your firm look incompetent and amateurish—not a good image to convey.

Remember that a computer screen has a much lower resolution than paper. Computer screens typically only have a resolution of 72 dots per inch. This value is much less than paper—even a cheap typesetting job can be 300 dots per inch. The consequence is that reading on a computer screen is slower (up to 25 percent slower) and more error-prone than reading from paper. Fortunately, there are some advantages to computer storage and hypertext that you can use to even up the score. The main advantage is that you can make available far more information than is possible with paper, and you can use hypertext to layer pages, allowing the viewer to decide when to go to the next layer for additional information.

Traditionally, **body copy,** or the main block of text in an ad, is used to explain benefits, present the solution to a problem, or to explain why the consumer should make a purchase. The copy varies in form from third person narrative, dialogue, testimonial, or drama. Active voice invariably works better than passive voice. Body copy is usually kept short, even on paper, for ads that are attempting to convey an image. Similarly, ads for convenience products are generally pretty concise as well. But it is natural to include more copy when the goal is to get the consumer to take some action. Likewise, ads for high involvement goods, or complex new products, need to be somewhat more verbose. Even so, keep in mind that you should focus on cutting the text down to be as concise as possible. And then after you have cut until you can't cut any more, reduce it even further. When you want to elaborate, break the text into smaller pieces. In other words, modularize by creating sub pages.

The Web allows you to present more information than paper since computer storage and dissemination is ultimately cheaper than storing and distributing information on paper. But the key to unlocking this advantage is to let your readers control how much of your information they want to see. You have to give visitors something that cannot be done on paper—the opportunity to *not* have everything in front of them all at once. The visitor is in charge—the visitor runs the show by clicking on links with his or her mouse.

As you are breaking your text up into modules, think about the audience. Using your market knowledge, answer the following question: Is there a certain logical sequence that buyers go through as they contemplate your product? As an example, consider the market for gardening products. Gardeners must prepare the ground, plant seeds, weed, fertilize, and then harvest the fruit (or vegetable) of their labor. Assuming that the consumers for gardening products think in this linear way, the sequence described offers a sensible model for organizing a promotional site in this product category.

Perhaps you sell different categories of products, such as printers, computers, and software. It could be logical to create different modules for each product category. However, it is important to organize your site in a manner consistent with the way the consumer thinks. It might be that people always think of your hardware and software together. Just because your company has two different divisions for these two types of products doesn't mean that this separation will be logical to the visitors to your site.

Another possibility is that you may have different segments of visitors with different interests. For example, a bicycle manufacturer could have two largely different audiences: those interested in racing or other athletic events, and those who need a bike to commute to work or school. The racing topics will not be interesting to the commuter group, and vice versa. Your main page could have a list of topics including racing and commuting. Each topic would have a very brief description, but a visitor could click on the description to get more in-depth information.

You might not know how the consumers categorize your products or how their interests could be categorized. Such ignorance makes it difficult to know the best way to break topics presented on your site into different modules. In that case, marketing research would be necessary. One fairly simple technique is to bring in a few consumers at a time, and get them to engage in free association. Free association is a technique originally used by psychologists wherein the researcher gives a word or phrase, and the subject says whatever comes into his mind first. You could use this method to figure out the categories that people naturally think of when they think of your product. Another technique you can use is to interview your firm's salespeople to ask them for insights into the ways that the consumers think about your company's offerings.

Hypertext is neither a linear nor a serial medium. All visitors do not move through your information space in the same sequence. One visitor might look at pictures of the different products first and look at the prices for each after viewing each picture. The next visitor might go over all the prices first, then look at several pictures. There may be nearly an infinite number of paths that different readers might take through your information space. The implication of this non-linearity is that your modules need to be self-contained. Since the reader can hit them in any order, you cannot assume that they have read the preliminary, fundamental modules first. You can help by making heavy use of cross-linking. In a site for stereo equipment, you might have separate modules for the CD players, the amplifiers, the speakers, and sound quality. This last module might refer to the technical details of the speakers that are only discussed in the speaker module. Hypertext lets you link to the relevant information in the other module. Allow your users to easily move from topic to topic on your site. A navigation bar is one good way to insure that visitors will be able to figure out how to maneuver in your site, even if they land on an obscure page that came up on a search engine.

Because reading on a computer screen is slow, Web users like to skim or scan text. You should write in the inverted pyramid style used by reporters. Start with the conclusions, and then follow with the most important support. Then add background information or supporting material. Your goal is to help the reader process rapidly and enjoyably what the page is about. If they are interested in pursuing one of the modules you provide, they have the opportunity to click and go to sub pages. Help them spot what they might want to pursue by highlighting keywords or providing emphasis with color.

You should make judicious use of nesting—many sections with numerous subsections. Make section headings instantly meaningful, not overly cute, and certainly don't write headings with hyperbole.

Some kinds of material naturally work well in an electronic environment. Don't hesitate to include glossaries, lists, histories, bibliographies, or technical specifications. Remember, by letting the user control how much he or she sees, you will not be burdening them.

If you think a significant portion of your audience will want to print parts of your Web site, you might consider having two versions: one for online viewing and a separate version for printing. The version optimized for printing would have much longer modules since it is not convenient to print many small modules. A PDF or Acrobat file is ideal for creating printable versions of online text.

Summary

1.   WWW copy needs to be of a different style than the language used on TV and other media.
2.   Computer screens are harder to read than paper. Copy must therefore be short and suitable for skimming by the visitor.
3.   Write in an inverted pyramid style for the Web with pages, sub-pages, sub-sub-pages, and so on.

Online Activities

Visit the companion Web site at www.wiley.com/college/hofacker for chapter summaries, examples, hypertext cases, homework assignments, text material updates, research exercises, and *Wall Street Journal Interactive Edition* access.

GO TO   http://www.wiley.com/college/hofacker

 THE WALL STREET JOURNAL.

References

Bonime, Andrew and Ken C. Pohlman, *Writing for New Media*, Wiley, 1998.

Lewis, Herschell Gordon and Jamie Murphy (1998) *Cybertalk That Sells*, Chicago: Contemporary Books.

Mills, Carol B. and Linda J. Weldon (1987) Reading Text from Computer Screens, *ACM Computing Surveys*, 19 (December), 329-358.

Muter, Paul and Paula Maurutto (1991) Reading and Skimming from Computer Screens and Books: The Paperless Office Revisited? *Behaviour and Information Technology,* 10 (July/August), 257-266.

Nash, Edward L. (1995) *Direct Marketing: Strategy, Planning, Execution*, New York: McGraw Hill.

Wright, Peter and Alan Lickorish (1983) Proof-Reading Texts on Screen and on Paper, *Behaviour and Information Technology*, 2 (July/September), 227-235.

Chapter 10

ADVERTISING BANNERS

LEARNING OBJECTIVES

1. Understand how a company's communication goals translate into ad banners.
2. Assess the importance of the hosting page, the banner itself, and the pay-off page.

Advertising exists almost everywhere in today's world, so it is hardly surprising that a great deal of advertising appears on World Wide Web pages. An advertising banner is usually a small rectangular image with some clickable graphics and text. Banners often appear on a content site, one that offers something helpful or fun for the visitor. Clicking on a banner generally takes the viewer to the advertiser's Web site.

When contemplating using an ad banner, think through what your goals for the banner might be. Generally speaking, the goals of advertising fall into one of the following three consumer processes:

1. *Cognition.* The banner could be designed to facilitate awareness, knowledge, or active thinking about the brand. A banner could have this kind of benefit even if the consumer does not click on it.

2. *Affect.* The ad could focus on emotion, interest, feelings, or desire. It is difficult to achieve a change in a consumer's affect with just a banner ad; you need to draw them to your site for a real effect.

3. *Behavior.* The ad might be designed to induce an action on the part of the consumer, such as an initial sale or an accelerated or repeated transaction. Most banner ads are designed to simply get the consumer to click through. After the consumers arrive at the site, the real advertising campaign begins.

A firm's strategy and current market conditions dictate which of these three approaches should receive short-run emphasis. Since different consumers are in different places with respect to cognition, affect, and behavior, not all ad campaigns work for all consumers. But the bottom line is that your Web advertising banner needs to play a part in furthering one of the above goals.

The banner itself is just one link in a well-coordinated tactical chain with three links. First, there is the page that hosts the banner. Second, there is the execution of the banner itself, including images and copy. Third, there is the payoff page that visitors see when they click on the banner.

The Hosting Page

We might as well call it the "splinternet." Not so long ago cable TV executives were talking enthusiastically about "500 channels." The Internet dwarfs that capability—it is like cable TV with millions of channels! Consequently, you cannot use the same strategy for advertising on the Internet as you might with a mass medium like TV. The Internet is not a mass medium, it is a niche medium. The taste and the demand for information is more heterogeneous, or variable, than the demand for other products since uses of information can vary so greatly from one consumer to another. The Internet is allowing for the heterogeneity of taste like nothing else that has come before.

Table 10.1 is a hypothetical table meant to provide a feel for the size and use of the Web within the next few years.

Looking at the very last row of the table, presume there is one site, perhaps Yahoo!, that will host 1 billion visits per month. There may be 10 sites that receive 100 million visits per month. As you move up each row of the table, there is one-tenth as many visitors and 10 more times as many sites. Finally, at the top of the table there are perhaps a billion pages that might have one person per month look at them.

Table 10-1
Hypothetical Distribution of Web Visitors

Number of Visits per Month	Number of Sites with That Many Visits
1	1,000,000,000
10	100,000,000
100	10,000,000
1,000	1,000,000
10,000	100,000
100,000	10,000
1,000,000	1,000
10,000,000	100
100,000,000	10
1,000,000,000	1

Mass media-based thinking might have us focus on the one site that gets 1 billion visits and try to produce a blanket campaign. But it is hopeless to try to use banners to achieve huge numbers of impressions as is done with TV. There are just too many sites out there. But what a banner *can* do very well is to get you a very targeted audience. Why waste computer time and network connections for people who might click on your banner but then back out immediately? Especially when you are the advertiser and you are paying the bills! It makes more sense to focus on the one or two sites that have 10,000 or 100,000 targeted visitors who best match your intended audience. That way you use the Internet for what it is good for—bringing a smaller but more targeted group of people to your site to stay for a while and then make return visits.

The key to executing this strategy is to look for synergy between your goals and the sites you can use to display your banner. You want to match the lifestyle and interests of the viewers of the site to your market and focus down to a niche. For example, the manufacturer of tennis rackets does not need to be content with sponsoring general sports sites like www.espn.go.com or www.cnnsi.com. Instead, it would make the best use of the Internet to focus on sites such as www.tenniscountry.com, a site that describes itself as the "total tennis" site on the Internet.

Some other factors to consider:

Seek exclusivity of advertising for the product category with the site selling the banner space. In other words, Ford would not want Chevrolet to advertise on a site where it bought advertising.

Negotiate for a preferred position on the page. Generally, the upper left corner is the most noticed part of a page.

Ask for a free trial period to help you figure out whether the cost will be worth the results.

Within certain limits, the size of the ad is not that important, other than the fact that a bigger ad allows you to include more copy.

The more targeted the audience, the more you will be charged for hosting a banner, but you should be willing to pay more for a more targeted audience.

After you have picked out some likely hosting sites for your banner, the next consideration will be cost. When companies started to think about advertising on the Web, the most natural way to set ad prices was the same way ad rates are set in the mass media. In the mass media, the advertiser pays the content provider, such as a magazine or television station, based on how many people are exposed to the ad. Pricing in this manner is called **CPM Pricing**. CPM refers to Cost Per thousand, with the "M" meaning "thousand" like the Roman numeral for 1,000. When this method is applied to the Web, the advertiser pays according to how many thousands of people visit the page on which the ad resides. However, just because a banner appeared on the page does not mean that a consumer saw, noticed, or thought about the banner.

More recently, the interactive nature of the Web has come to the forefront with a pricing approach called **click-through pricing**. In click-through pricing, the advertiser pays according to how many visitors click on the banner. From the advertiser's point of view, they are paying only for a result. The number of click-throughs directly measures the interactive pull of the ad in the page environment in which the ad appears and better suggests a monetary value for the hosting service.

Another proposed pricing mechanism is called **outcome-based pricing**. In this case, the advertiser pays by how many visitors brought in via clicking on the banner achieve some outcome, like a certain number of pages visited on the advertiser's site or a sale.

The Ad Banner

Figuring out what the banner should say, and how it should say it, requires that you contemplate your goals as described in the beginning of this chapter. Your choice of message, and of how the banner should look, depends on whether the goal of the advertising thrust is cognitive, affective, or behavioral. Most often, the immediate goal of the banner is to produce a click that results in a visit to the advertiser's site. However, a well-designed banner ad could leave the visitor with some knowledge about the product (a cognitive result) or with a positive image of the company (an affective result). Thus, the banner might be able to contribute to your goal even if it is not clicked on. Generally, though, a small banner limits what you can convey, and the main role of a banner is to get visitors to your site where you can really make an impression.

For the banner to have any impact at all, first it needs to attract the attention of the page visitor. Animation is a good eye-catcher. You will also want to make sure that the colors chosen for the banner contrast with the colors used for the hosting page. The ability of a banner to attract attention—and clicks—wears out rapidly for any given visitor, so it is a good idea to rotate several different versions of your banner.

If your goal is behavioral, designing the ad banner is complex. In that case, not all clicks are equally valuable. If the goal of the campaign is to get sales, you want targeted or qualified visitors to click on the banner, not site tourists who take a brief look around and hit the Back button. You must persuade the right type of consumer to click; otherwise you are wasting viewers' time and your computer and network resources.

The persuasive power of the banner to induce a visitor to click can work through one or both of two routes. The **central route** relies on logic. In this route, the consumer elaborates on the information in the ad and thinks about it in terms of his or her previous attitudes. For this elaboration to take place, the consumer must be interested and motivated about the topic. Here, a key requirement for clicking to take place has to do with the quality of the relevant information presented on the banner.

The **peripheral route** relies on attractiveness and emotion, or sometimes extremely simple inferences ("if so many people click on it, it must be cool").

Beautiful scenery or other images that create warm feelings rub off on the message of the ad. When the viewer is more passive, elements of the brand or ad become can become associated with positive emotion. With the peripheral route, the viewer is not doing much thinking about the message; in other words, they are not engaging in cognitive elaboration.

Whichever route you use, produce something that is compelling to click on, that creates a call to action. In order to successfully ask someone to leave the site they are visiting, you must create an expectation about the value of clicking using what a leading theorist of hypertext application and design, Brown University's George Landow has called, "the rhetoric of departure."

The Payoff Page

Now you have attracted visitors to your site. "The rhetoric of arrival" needs to be used to create a payoff page. The payoff page must meet the expectation created by the banner or visitors will just use their back button after cursory scanning. Of course your should never draw banner click-through visitors to a generic page. In an interactive medium you have the ability to customize and change everything. Put them on a special page that leverages the fact that you know where they just came from. For example, if you are running an ad banner for your tennis racket off of an article about Michael Chang, the page might contain an endorsement of the racket by Chang. An ad banner for mortgage services running in a real estate classifieds site could lead to a page with a mortgage payment calculator. The key is to create a synergy between the hosting page, the payoff page, and the execution of the ad banner itself. Networked computers are much smarter than TVs or paper. Leverage that intelligence!

Summary

1. Advertising with banners on the Internet is quite different than mass media advertising. The Internet is niche medium.
2. Internet ad banners can work through either the peripheral or central routes to persuasion.
3. There should be synergy between the hosting page, the ad banner copy, and the payoff page.

Online Activities

Visit the companion Web site at www.wiley.com/college/hofacker for chapter summaries, examples, hypertext cases, homework assignments, text material updates, research exercises, and *Wall Street Journal Interactive Edition* access.

GO TO   http://www.wiley.com/college/hofacker

THE WALL STREET JOURNAL.

References

Chatterjee, Patrali, Donna L. Hoffman and Thomas P. Novak (1998) Modeling the Clickstream: Implications for Web-Based Advertising Efforts, Working Paper, http://www2000.ogsm.vanderbilt.edu/.

Barry, Thomas E. and Daniel J. Howard (1990) A Review and Critique of the Hierarchy of Effects in Advertising, *International Journal of Advertising*, 9, 121-135.

Briggs, Rex and Nigel Hollis (1997). Advertising on the Web: Is There Response Before Click-Through? *Journal of Advertising Research*, 37 (March-April), 33-45.

Drèze, Xavier and Fred Zufryden (1998) Is Internet Advertising Ready for Prime Time? *Journal of Advertising Research*, 38, (May/June).

Ducoffe, Robert H. (1996) Advertising Value and Advertising on the Web, *Journal of Advertising Research*, 36 (September/October), 21-35.

Hofacker, Charles F. and Jamie Murphy (1998) World Wide Web Banner Advertisement Copy Testing, *European Journal of Marketing,* 32 (7/8), 703-712.

Hughes, G. D. Realtime Response Measures Redefine Advertising Wearout, *Journal of Advertising Research*, 32 (May/June), 61-77.

Janiszewski, Chris (1996) The Influence of Display Characterisitics on Visual Exploratory Search Behavior, Working Paper, University of Florida.

Lord, Kenneth R., Myung-Soo Lee and Paul L Sauer (1995) The Combined Influence Hypothesis: Central and Peripheral Antecedents of Attitude toward the Ad, *Journal of Advertising,* 14 (Spring), 73-85.

Petty, Richard E. and Joseph R. Priester. "Mass Media Attitude Change: Implications of the Elaboration Likelihood Model of Persuasion," in Bryant, Jennings and Dolf Zillmann (Eds.), *Media Effects: Advances in Theory and Research*, Hillsdale, NJ: Lawrence Erlbaum Associates, 1994.

Robertson, Thomas S. (1976) Low Commitment Consumer Behavior, *Journal of Advertising Research*, 16 (April), 19-27.

Raman, N. V. and J. D. Lekeny (1995) Advertising on Interactive Media: Some Issues, Some Suggestions, *Proceedings of the American Academy of Advertising*, 247-251.

Smith, Robert. E. and William. R. Swinyard (1982) Information Response Models: An Integrated Approach, Journal of Marketing, 46 (Winter), 81-93.

Voight, Joan (1996) Beyond the Banner, *Wired*, 4 (December), 196-204.

Yuan, Yuehong, Jonathan P. Caulkins and Stephen Roehrig (1998) The Relationship Between Advertising and Content on the Internet, *European Journal of Marketing*, 32 (7/8), 677-687.

Part III
COMPUTER-MEDIATED SELLING

Chapter 11

SHOPPING ON THE INTERNET

LEARNING OBJECTIVES

1. Learn about direct marketing.
2. Become familiar with the several types of risk perceived by Web shoppers.
3. Evaluate the importance of consumer choice processing, especially consumer search.

Much marketing activity occurs through some kind of channel. Products move from a manufacturer to a wholesaler and then to a retailer. But long before the Internet, companies used catalogs to create a *compressed channel* with no intermediary. Then came toll-free numbers, the fax machine, and shopping-oriented cable television stations. These technologies allowed manufacturers to sell directly to individuals.

Many companies use direct marketing and also other forms of selling. Like IBM, you can have a sales force and use direct marketing, or like Sears, you can have both retail and catalog sales. If your company engages in more than one form of selling, it is important to coordinate an overall marketing plan. You don't want your sales force to become demoralized as Internet sales increase and it becomes harder to meet their personal sales goals. Similarly, if you have a catalog and an Internet selling presence, the two should be used to complement, not compete with, each other.

In recent years, direct marketing has grown faster than retailing. Consumers today have less time to shop. Congestion and the difficulties of parking continue to increase. Retailers have not helped themselves any by hiring unqualified help at the minimum wage. Often retail help consists of disinterested clerks poorly trained to facilitate customer satisfaction. Even though retail square footage is up, retail profit per square foot is down. Further, retailing is now dominated by large chains that tend to drop slower-moving specialty items in the interest of efficiency. Direct marketing, and particularly Internet selling, has the advantage of being available 24 hours per day, 7 days per week. The widespread availability of 24- and 48-hour delivery by businesses such as FedEx, Airborne Express, DHL, and

UPS has also enabled quick purchase turnaround. Combined, all of these factors have left the door wide open to niche direct-marketing specialists, Internet-based or otherwise.

A 2 percent response to a direct mailing is considered a good response rate. On the Internet, the percentage of visitors to a site who actually purchase something may be substantially less than that. For example, one firm with a selling site is in the personal services business. During a recent time period, the firm found that of every 100,000 visitors to their site, the firm makes approximately 300 sales, which is a 0.3 percent response rate. But since the network and computing power required to handle 100,000 visitors is so inexpensive, the site is still profitable despite the relatively low amount of purchasing.

Response rates can be improved with good "copy," or text. Direct marketers always say, "Fire a big gun to start a war." Don't do a warm-up. Lead off with copy that will stop the browser in her tracks. Question-oriented copy works well, and copy that has a direct implication for the viewer, as in, "click here if you want . . ." The copy should appeal to needs or create desire—and point out how the benefits of your offering can satisfy those needs and desires. If you can anticipate obstacles to the sale, address those somewhere in the middle, not at the beginning or end of your pitch.

Be careful not to think in terms of the hard selling that is frequently practiced in the broadcast media. Compared to TV, which tends to be superficial with a premium paid to visual attractiveness, the Web is customer- and thinking-dominated. Don't insult the visitor with overblown prose and clichés. Since Web browsers tend to skim, not read, you want terse phrasing of the sort that might appear in a good classified advertisement.

Simple language is preferable when you want to take a cognitive or thinking route to persuasion. This would be the case for business-to-business marketing, computers or electronics, entertainment, or fundraising. Sophisticated language works better for autos, fashion, houses, liquor, or other lifestyle products where a peripheral or emotional persuasion strategy would be indicated.

You need to ask for their order *now*. In an interactive medium, timeliness is critical. Provide a reason, perhaps with an offer that will expire, why your viewer should click on the purchase button right now.

Currently the quality of graphics on the Internet is inferior to those that can be found in a catalog. That means that even though you may be able to offer something of a nonverbal message with images, the enthusiasm has to be made up for in the copy.

And who will be reading that copy? Direct marketers have known that "in-home buyers" are more confident, adventurous, innovative, price-conscious, and cosmopolitan than those who do not buy at home. In addition, these consumers do not perceive risk in buying directly.

Perceived Risk and Trust

Direct marketers who use catalogs or toll-free phone numbers have long had to deal with the issues of risk and trust. The Internet adds some twists to these issues since purchasing a product online poses many unique risks to the consumer.

First there is **time risk**. The consumer may fear that he or she will waste time going to a site. Since many sites are overloaded with graphics and are difficult to navigate, a consumer could burn up a lot of time just trying to find and purchase a product.

Second, there is **vendor risk**—that the site they are visiting might be a sham—a bogus site just set up to rip them off. In real shopping, the physical setting tends to be somewhat reassuring. At least there is a place they can go to complain if there is a problem. Not so on the Internet. The lack of tangibility can make consumers nervous. The successful online vendors will be those that create a solid sense of trust. Creating trust can be facilitated by connecting your site to the solid, offline world. You should include your address, phone number, and ticker symbol under company information for concerned consumers looking for reassurance. Joining the Better Business Bureau and provided its phone number might be another good tactic, along with including links or contact information to satisfied customers. In some cases, you may be able to partner with a well-known vendor and this can act to allay consumer fear about you.

There is also **security risk,** which is a fear by consumers they will be the victim of some kind of computer crime, perhaps involving their credit card number or the private information provided to the vendor. Security risk is particularly critical for firms offering online financial services. Hackers represent an ongoing menace, and the threat of computer crime has surely been well-documented by the mass media.

Just as in other forms of direct marketing, there is **brand risk**—that the specific brand they are buying will have problems. Generally, brand risk is eliminated when selling well-known national brands.

There is the **risk to privacy.** Optimal use of the online medium requires informational exchange between the firm and the consumer. But visitors to a selling site have concerns about privacy. People are especially troubled by the idea that personal information they reveal could be sold and used by other companies.

Trust is essential in facilitating exchange. Consumers need to have three kinds of trust before they will buy:

> Trust in the mechanics of the selling process.
> Trust in the fairness and integrity of the specific people involved.
> Trust in the firm or the institution and its ability to fulfill its delivery promise.

If they trust you, they will be willing to provide you information so long as it is not sold to a third party. The fact that you have that information does not bother them. For example, few consumers become alarmed when they order from a Web site a second time and their shipping address automatically appears.

Consumer Choice and Search

Researchers who study consumer choice have long known that the actual act of choosing is just one of several of steps consumers go through when they buy. These steps can take a lot of time and effort, or not, depending on the level of involvement that the buyer feels with the decision. The decision to purchase begins in the mind of the consumer as a gap between what they want and what they have. This requires some kind of recognition or awareness that they have a want. Once someone has this realization, he or she may begin to search for a product or service that can satisfy the want. The effort put into the search may be trivial. It may be that the search consists of a quick scan of the shelf of the nearest convenience store. Or the search could take years.

The extent of search engaged in for any particular purchase is determined by a large number of factors in which involvement is one important key. Other factors determining the extent of search include personal relevance, perceived risk, price, length of commitment, conspicuousness of the purchase, safety, time pressure, the number and types of different brands that must be researched and the existence of other linked purchasing decisions. All consumers do not engage in searches all the time because there is a downside to search—namely, that it takes time. It delays the decision and therefore it delays the benefits of the purchase. There is also an opportunity cost to the time and money spent searching. Of course, the speed and flexibility of the Internet tends to reduce the psychological and economic costs of search to the consumer.

Consumers search when they feel they need to reduce uncertainty about a purchase. The more experience and confidence a consumer has in his or her knowledge, the less they need to search. Consumers also vary in terms of where they like to seek information with some preferring personal advice from family or friends, some preferring to visit stores, some enjoying reading consumer-oriented periodicals, and some preferring online search.

Because the Internet allows consumers to search quickly and cheaply, we will see a general increase in the amount of search going on in all kinds of markets, but especially in markets for information-rich products. Intangible or symbolic information products such as airline tickets actually gain tangibility online. An Internet site like www.travelocity.com can get the consumer closer to the service by offering travel planning help, graphs, lists of flights, and reviews of hotels.

The Internet will allow people to more easily find products that uniquely match their tastes, and do so from the comfort and security of their own homes. In addition to the sheer efficiency of Internet searching, other advantages to online shopping lie in the sheer number of alternatives that the consumer is able to consider, and the ease with which the quality and prices of alternatives can be compared. Online retailers can facilitate the process by allowing searching and sorting of offerings within a Web site. Of course, the other side of the coin is that a third-party search site might allow comparisons across Web sites so that competing offers from competing sites could be easily compared.

Unless the search tools are well designed however, the consumer might find himself in the throes of information overload. In that case, too much information can inhibit a decision. Under these conditions, the consumer sometimes ignores important information as new data pour in.

Goods can be categorized depending on the amount of search typically exhibited:

Convenience goods are purchased where available. Consumers frequently will not seek out particular brands. When these commodity goods are bought online, price is the key factor.

Specialty goods engender strong brand preferences. Consumers will search for an online store carrying a particular brand. Examples include instruments, art supplies, and bikes. Online retailers can compete on price, but other factors such as service and convenience can be brought to bear.

Shopping goods inspire prepurchase searches on the part of consumers to learn about products, options, and prices. Examples here might include home appliances or stereo equipment. Extensive and informative Web pages can create a competitive advantage for this type of online retailer.

The quality of online offerings can only be compared for some characteristics. We need to distinguish between the following types of product characteristics.

Search characteristics are claims or characteristics you can evaluate while searching or shopping. It is important to reveal as many of these as possible, since they may differentiate your offerings from those of your competitor's. Fortunately the Web allows you to store far more information about the characteristics of your products than would be feasible on paper. Of course, what qualifies as a search characteristic on a retail expedition around town does not necessarily constitute an Internet search characteristic. It doesn't take a retailing genius to know that the Internet does not have the capacity to convey touch and feel. And even though the quality of graphics is poor when compared to print, you could provide a thumbnail for most visitors and more detailed visual information for those motivated to seek it out.

Experience characteristics can only be evaluated after purchase. In order to successfully sell products with important experience characteristics, you are going to have to think carefully about guarantees, and service and return policy. Here, word of mouth, references and customer referrals can work to your advantage and it could be worthwhile to provide discounts to customers who bring in other customers. If your product includes experience attributes, you might benefit from encouraging an active virtual community on your site as discussed in Chapter 6.

HTML Sidebar

The <META> tag is used to set up keywords that will allow search engines to find your page more easily. The format of the <META> markup follows next.

You would replace *word1* and *word2* and so forth with words you think a consumer would choose if they were looking for what you sell.

```
<META HTTP-EQUIV="Keywords" CONTENT="word1,word2,...">
```

Credence characteristics represent attributes the consumer will never be able to evaluate, like the quality of a weld, or the stitching used in a carpet.

When confronted with a new technology, it is tempting to carry forward older concepts. Some companies carried forward the metaphor of physical space into cyberspace and set up Internet malls. But consumers do not say to themselves, "I think I'll visit Joe's Mall and search around to see what they have to sell." Instead, consumers do a specific search on the product category they are interested in. Consequently, online retailers need to make sure each product is well represented in the output of search engine searches.

One way to do this is by including **key words** in your pages that you think people will use when searching for what you sell. You need to figure out what key words to include. In fact, the HTML log record tells you the key words a consumer used when he or she used a search engine and found you. Sadly, this reminiscent of the engineers who were studying World War II fighter planes that had been shot but managed to limp back to their base. The plan was to reinforce the planes in the places where they found bullet holes. One day a veteran pilot saw them carefully recording where the bullets had hit. He asked them what they were doing. When they told him he said, "You should reinforce the planes in the places where there are no bullet holes." The point was that the planes that never made it back to base were presumably hit in different places. Unfortunately, log files cannot tell you the phrases consumers used when they were looking for you and did *not* find you. But at least it is simple to do some qualitative research in which you watch some consumers search for products related to what you sell.

There are some legal and ethical issues using key words. Suppose I am a small competitor of Kodak. Can I or should I put the word "Kodak" somewhere on my page so that my page turns up when people search on Kodak? These and some other legal questions are addressed in Chapter 17, and tactics that help a searcher find your site are also discussed in the section on hedonic versus utilitarian visitors. For now, we turn to the final stages of the consumer choice process: alternative evaluation, purchase and postpurchase.

Products and services can be thought of as bundles of features or collections of attributes. A vacation package is a bundle that includes a certain kind of accommodation, a specific destination, and a particular travel mode. The consumer might compare a set of brands based on their attributes. Some comparisons are **compensatory,** meaning that a brand can make up for a bad score on one attribute with a good score on another attribute. When employing compensatory evaluation, the consumer takes into account not only beliefs about the attributes for each brand, but the importance of the attributes as well. Sometimes consumers employ **elimination rules** whereby a product is removed from consideration if it does not meet a certain minimum requirement.

Regardless of the consumer's evaluation strategy, computer-based presentation could make it easy to compare alternatives on many attributes. A search process allows a consumer to sequentially compare various alternatives while a page with multiple thumbnail representations could allow them to proceed with a simultaneous look at all the products.

The purchase itself needs to be as easy as possible for the consumer, and this topic is discussed in Chapter 14. Also, note that what happens after purchase can be very important for repeat business and so your site could have lots of information that will make the purchase more valuable to the consumer, as well as enhance the relationship between you and that customer. This topic was discussed in Chapter 6.

Summary

1. The amount of consumer search depends on the individual and various psychological and economic factors.
2. Different products require different amounts and types of searches.
3. Consumers face time risk, vendor risk, security risk, privacy risk, and brand risk when they shop on the Internet.
4. In-home sellers have some advantages, and disadvantages, when compared to traditional retailers.

Online Activities

Visit the companion Web site at www.wiley.com/college/hofacker for chapter summaries, examples, hypertext cases, homework assignments, text material updates, research exercises, and *Wall Street Journal Interactive Edition* access.

GO TO   http://www.wiley.com/college/hofacker

References

Bateson, J. E. G. (1985) The Self-Service Customer - Empirical Findings, *Journal of Retailing*, 51 (3), 49-76.

Beatty, Sharon E. and Scott M. Smith (1987) External Search Effort An Investigation Across Several Product Categories, *Journal of Consumer Research*, 14 (1), 83-95.

Card, Stuart K., Thomas P. Moran and Alan Newell (1983) *The Psychology of Human-Computer Interaction*, Hillsdale, NJ: Lawrence Erlbaum Associates, Inc.

Carson, Stephen J., Joann J. Peck and Terry L. Childers (1996) Preliminary Results on the Determinants of Technology Assisted Shopping (TAS): A Model, Measure Development, and Validation, *Proceedings of the 1996 AMA Winter Educators' Conference*.

Comer, James M., Raj Mehta, and Terence Holmes (1998) Information Technology: Retail Users Versus Nonusers, *Journal Of Interactive Marketing*, 12 (2), 49-62.

Hilton, Chadwick B., William H. Motes and John S. Fielden (1989), An Experimental Study of the Effects of Style and Organization on Reader Perceptions of Text, *Journal of Business Communication,* 26, (Summer), 255-270.

Hearst, Marti A. (1997) Interfaces for Searching the Web, *Scientific American*, (March), 68-72.

Kelley, S. W., J. H. Donnelly and S. J. Skinner (1990) Customer Participation in Service Production and Delivery, *Journal of Retailing*, 66 (Fall), 315-335.

Klein, Lisa (1998) Evaluating the Potential of Interactive Media Through a New Lens: Search Versus Experience Goods, *Marketing Letters ,* 9 (3), 195-203.

Lewis, Herschell Gordon and Robert D. Lewis. *Selling on the Net*. NTC Business Books: Chicago, 1997.

Lohse, Gerald L. and Eric J. Johnson (1996) A Comparison of Two Process Tracing Methods for Choice Tasks, *Organizational Behavior and Human Decision Processe*s. 68 (October), 28-43.

Lumpkin, J. R. Retailing Without Stores: An Examination of Catalog Shoppers, *Journal of Business Research*, 13, 139-151.

McCorkle, D. E. (1990) The Role of Perceived Risk in Mail Order Catalog Shopping, *Journal of Direct Marketing*, 4 (Autumn), 26-35.

Mehta, Abhilasha (1994) How Advertising Response Modeling (ARM) Can Increase Ad Effectiveness, *Journal of Advertising Research*, (May/June), 62-74.

Moorthy, Sridhar, Brian T. Ratchford and Debabrata Talukdar (1997) Consumer Information Search Revisited: Theory and Empirical Analyses, *Journal of Consumer Research*, 23 (March), 263-277.

Motes, William H., Chadwick B. Hilton and John S. Fielden (1992) Language, Sentence and Structural Variations in Print Advertising, *Journal of Advertising Research*, (September/October), 63-77.

Nash, Edward L. *Direct Marketing: Strategy, Planning, Execution*. New York: McGraw-Hill, 1995.

Novak, Thomas P., Donna L. Hoffman and Marcos Peralta (1999) Building Consumer Trust in Online Environments: The Case for Information Privacy, *Communications of the ACM*, In press.

Rossiter, John R. (1981) Predicting Starch Scores, *Journal of Advertising Research*, 21 (October), 63-68.

Shaver, Dick. *The Next Step in Database Marketing: Consumer Guided Marketing*. New York: Wiley, 1996.

Shugan, Steven M. (1980) The Cost of Thinking, *Journal of Consumer Research*, 7 (2), 99-111.

Simpson, L. and H. B. Lakner (1993) Perceived Risk and Mail Order Shopping for Apparel, *Journal of Consumer Studies and Home Economics,* 17, 377-398.

Srinivasan, Narasimhan and Brian T. Ratchford (1991) An Empirical Test of a Model of External Search for Automobiles, *Journal of Consumer Research*, 18 (September), 233-242.

Van den Poel, Dirk and Joseph Leunis (1996) Perceived Risk and Risk Reduction Strategies in Mail-Order Versus Retail Store Buying, *The International Review of Retail, Distribution and Consumer Research*, 6 (4), 351-371.

Zeithaml, Valarie A., Leonard L. Berry and A. Parasuraman (1993) The Nature and Determinants of Customer Expectations of Service, *Journal of the Academy of Marketing Science*, 21 (Winter), 1-12.

Widing, Robert E. and W. Wayne Talarzyk (1993) Electronic Information Systems for Consumers: An Evaluation of Computer-Assisted Formats in Multiple Decision Environments, *Journal of Marketing Research*, 30 (May), 125-141.

Chapter 12

BUSINESS-TO-BUSINESS
INTERNET MARKETING

LEARNING OBJECTIVES

1. Learn how the Internet accelerates the automation of business-to-business transactions.
2. Understand how the Internet facilitates just-in-time inventory management.
3. Learn how the Internet facilitates outsourcing.
4. Learn some of the difficulties of using the Web for international marketing.

Many of the transactions that occur on the Internet are business-to-business transactions. Businesses are well-suited to take advantage of the Internet as a mechanism for reducing purchasing costs. Many companies have extensive local area networks and high-speed Internet gateways. Such facilities allow employees to quickly and easily search, choose, and buy. Firms such as Gateway, Cisco, and Sun Microsystems are finding that an increasing number of their business to business sales are executed over the Internet. In fact, most of the dollar volume in Internet commerce is from business-to-business sales. Of course, sales forces and toll-free numbers will not disappear in the big picture of business-to-business marketing, but the Internet is taking its place as one more important buying and selling tool.

Before the Internet burst into the awareness of corporate information technology specialists, a small number of firms previously cooperated electronically using a technique called **Electronic Data Interchange (EDI)**. EDI had the advantage of being relatively secure because it used closed private connections between two businesses. It was also reliable, but subject to infrequent cataclysmic failure. Since EDI software was proprietary rather than following open standards, it had to be custom built from scratch for each pair of firms using the technique. Naturally, this made it quite expensive. The Internet protocol has changed all of that by creating a standard way for any firm, no matter how small, to coordinate with other companies.

In effect, the inexpensive tools with which we are all familiar, such as the Web, chat, and email lists, can be used to create many different and flexible ways for firms to cooperate. An **electronic hierarchy** can be used where one of the firms in the channel maintains control by assuming a dominant position in a partnership or alliance. Or a decentralized **electronic market** can be used with price acting as the mechanism to control the flow of goods and services between firms. In the next section, we will focus on the trend toward electronic markets in business-to-business relationships. In the section after that, we cover how the Internet provides an impetus to just-in-time inventory techniques. Both of these trends require the buying and selling companies to closely coordinate—coordination that the Internet makes easier to achieve.

The Internet Gives an Impetus to Outsourcing

Firms frequently face a choice between doing something themselves or buying the service from another firm, a practice commonly called outsourcing. Outsourcing is often the less-expensive option as the various selling firms that have to compete to sell their services end up being more efficient at production than in-house operations. Further efficiencies are created by the economics of scale. In other words, when a company does one thing many times for many other companies, it learns how to do it cheaper, better, and faster than a single company could do it for itself. Production costs go down.

There is a downside to outsourcing. The buying firm loses some control. It is harder to coordinate transactions in an external market than in an internal hierarchy. The buying company must search for a vendor; specify, negotiate, and monitor contracts; and handle financial settlement. Specification is particularly difficult when the product or service in question is specific and unique, rather than a simple commodity of some kind. There are several burdens on the selling firm as well. The seller must spend money on advertisements and other marketing activities. In other words, the administrative costs of outsourcing tend to be higher than for in-house goods or services. Sellers also face the temptation of taking advantage of the buying firm by raising prices if it has specific and unique needs, or if it is time-consuming or expensive to switch to another vendor.

The Internet will facilitate an increase in the amount of business outsourcing because the Internet reduces many of the administrative problems outlined above. Physically separated companies can communicate and organize themselves into virtual buying pools, leveraging their combined size to get the most advantageous arrangement from selling firms. The Internet reduces the cost of searching for vendors, making it easier to find alternative sellers and to switch to them. Negotiation becomes far less time consuming as the Internet adds several flexible alternatives, synchronous and asynchronous, to the mix of communications channels, such as chat, Web pages, and email. In addition to facilitating coordination, more communications options and richer forms of communication allow firms to build up trust in one another. This communication enhances the relationship between firms and engenders a sense of commitment. The coming of age of Internet video will only further accelerate this trend.

IP is emerging as the base organizing principle for linking business devices of all kinds, be they external connections over the Internet or internal connections via an intranet. Hand-held scanners, computers, and printers can be used for contract monitoring, inventory assessment, warehousing, or invoicing. Errors can be reduced and quickly caught when they are made. And all of these functions can be integrated. The ease with which various automated systems can "speak to" each other will be paralleled by the ease with which humans from different firms can communicate by email, chat, or the Web.

In recent years, firms have applied Internet technology to their internal communications needs. Internal Internets are often called **intranets**, with "intra" signifying that the network is used within the firm. An intranet is simply the use of IP and its attendant services—email, chat, Web sites, and streaming technology—for internal company use. Generally access to these intra-firm services is restricted, by various mechanisms, to employees. All in all this technology has allowed firms to be more flexible and to decentralize their decision making because it has enhanced idea generation and coordination, making relationships between employees all the better suited to reacting quickly to fast changing market conditions. In a similar manner, when two or more companies use dedicated Internet technology to facilitate communication between them, this sort of communications infrastructure is called an **extranet**. Companies participating in an extranet can benefit as their relationship becomes more fluid and adaptable, helping them to administer and coordinate the flow of goods and services between them. Once firms achieve a higher level of information integration, it becomes easier to use an inventory philosophy originally pioneered in Japan, known as **just-in-time inventory**. As we shall now see, the challenges of this approach are increasingly surmountable with Internet information technology.

Just-in-Time Inventory

One way that businesses have reduced costs is through the just-in-time approach to inventory management. Companies that use this approach order inventory at the last minute, only as they need it. Until this method was used, firms maintained a large inventory of the parts and supplies needed to build their products or provide services. But keeping supplies in storage, unused costs money; there are storage, breakage, and depreciation costs. What's more, capital that could be used for other purposes remains tied up in inventory. So as a general rule, the less inventory you have to hold, the cheaper it is for you to do business. An additional advantage to holding a small amount inventory is that it lets companies adapt to changing market conditions faster and bring new products out sooner since there is much less of a penalty to changing production. Shipments can be customized from moment to moment.

The downside to the just-in-time approach is that it requires the supplier and the buyer to be very coordinated or the cost of numerous small transactions will eat up all the benefits of maintaining a small inventory. They also need to trust and be committed to each other because they are going to be engaging in frequent and long-term delivery. If the firms must constantly go through many small bidding and inspection processes they will find that again they have eaten into the advantages of small inventories.

But again, note that the Internet is an ideal way to facilitate coordination. And since communication is an important building block for creating trust and commitment in a relationship, the Internet can help with those factors as well. Firms that share timely and meaningful information increase trust, which in turn leads to more sharing. The Internet can be used to communicate market trends, price fluctuations, and product availability. It can be used to establish communication at various and multiple inter-firm levels. As mentioned above, as hand-held devices such as scanners become IP enabled, the burdens of tracking many small deliveries are reduced. Digital records of all of these sorts of communications can be saved, human to human and machine to machine, creating an institutional memory of the relational exchange even as individuals leave the interacting firms.

International Internet Marketing

The nature of the World Wide Web is such that any marketing Web page is automatically an international marketing Web page. If you are at all interested in serving all of the businesses or consumers who can buy from your site, this consideration might cause you to contemplate carefully the way your page is written. Of course, if you are not interested in marketing to people outside of your country, it would be thoughtful to be clear about that on your site so as to not waste anybody's time.

Before we begin thinking about how to make a site friendlier to foreign visitors, we have to realize that use of the Internet is somewhat spotty in many parts of the world. The areas of highest Internet penetration are countries where a majority of citizens speak English such as the United States, Canada, Australia, New Zealand and the United Kingdom. Scandinavian countries also have a solid Internet infrastructure. In much of the rest of the world, however, telephone service is very expensive, making dial-up access problematic. Further, in many countries local phone calls are not free, which of course adds greatly to the price of Internet access. There is also much resistance on the part of local telephone monopolies, as well as governmental resistance, to the idea of the Internet. The personal computer, the vehicle for Internet access, still has a low penetration level in many countries. Other problems that must be considered are the maze of trade regulations between countries and the lack of package delivery options in some. However, in places where retail options are restricted, the Internet might be used to leapfrog local distribution.

Even before you start your international foray, the Internet is an excellent source of marketing intelligence. You can look up tariff information, import and export statistics, government trade policies, competitive environmental factors, distribution system specifics, local laws, regulations, standards and specifications, and the size of various markets.

Assuming you wish to sell either to consumers or to businesses outside of your country, language and communication will generally present you with your biggest challenge. If you are not going to translate your pages into one or more target languages, at the least you should try minimize the difficulties for non-native readers of your language. Try to avoid prepositions, such as "in", "on", "at" or "under", that are notoriously difficult for language students to master. Use short sentences, avoid multiple clauses of any sort, and stick to a subject-verb-object sentence sequence. Sports metaphors and other phrases that require culture specific knowledge often fail to click with foreign visitors, so stay away from these.

If you are going to translate your page, do not scrimp on translation services. Time and time again multinational companies have been embarrassed by poor translation. In particular, firms often run into bad luck using a phrase that is harmless in English but turns out to have an unsavory idiomatic meaning in another tongue. Note that humor can be particularly dangerous and should probably be avoided unless you have a local language specialist on staff.

Even nonverbal Web elements can cause problems. For example, the use of the color white is more or less neutral in parts of the world, but in some countries in Asia it signifies death. So for example, a "white flag" might mean surrender in one country but it could imply something a bit more macabre in some other country. Icons or images that depend on some type of verbal pun can also be mystifying to other cultures such as the use a magnifying glass to signify "search," or a kitchen table to signify a "table of data." At this time software exists to help in internationalizing a site, but there is no replacement yet for a native speaker well versed in the target culture.

Summary

1. The Internet will further the trend toward outsourcing, allowing companies to sell many types of products and services to each other more efficiently than they can produce these for themselves.

2. The Internet will accelerate the trend toward just-in-time inventory management, making it easier to coordinate numerous transactions among firms.

3. The Internet is a global network—consumers from other countries can easily view your page. Selling to consumers outside of your own country can be difficult and requires serious thought about language.

Online Activities

Visit the companion Web site at www.wiley.com/college/hofacker for chapter summaries, examples, hypertext cases, homework assignments, text material updates, research exercises, and *Wall Street Journal Interactive Edition* access.

GO TO   http://www.wiley.com/college/hofacker

wsj.com **THE WALL STREET JOURNAL.**

References

Benjamin, Robert and Rolf Wigand (1995) Electronic Markets and Virtual Value Chains on the Information Superhighway, *Sloan Management Review*, 36 (Winter), 62-72.

Bennett, Roger (1997) Export Marketing and the Internet: Experiences of Web Site Use and Perceptions of Export Barriers Among UK Businesses. *International Marketing Review*, 14 (5), 324-344.

Bensaou, M. and N. Venkatraman (1996) Inter-Organizational Relationships and Information Technology: A Conceptual Synthesis and a Research Framework, *European Journal of Information Systems*, 5 (2), 84-91.

Frazier, Gary L., Robert E. Spekman and Charles R. O'Neal (1988) Just-In-Time Exchange Relationships in Industrial Markets, *Journal of Marketing*, 52 (3), 52-67.

Glazer, Rashi (1991) Marketing in an Information-Intensive Environment: Strategic Implications of Knowledge as an Asset, *Journal of Marketing*, 55 (October), 1-19.

Hamill, Jim (1997) The Internet and international marketing, *International Marketing Review*; 14 (5), 300-323

Hart, Paul and Carol Saunders (1997) Power and Trust: Critical Factors in the Adoption and use of Electronic Data Interchange, *Organization Science*, 8 (January/February), 23-42.

Holland, Christopher P. (1995) Cooperative Supply Chain Management: The Impact of Interorganizational Information Systems, *Journal of Strategic Information Systems*, 4 (2), 117-133.

Holland, Christopher P. and Geoffrey A. Lockett (1997) Mixed Mode Network Structures: The Strategic Use of Electronic Communication by Organizations, *Organization Science*, 8 (5), 475-488.

Honeycutt E. D., T. B. Flaherty, and K. Benassi (1998) Marketing industrial products on the Internet," *Industrial Marketing Management*, 27 (1), 63-72.

Johanson, Jan, Lars Hallen, and Nazeem Seyed-Mohamed (1991) Interfirm Adaption in Business Relationships, *Journal of Marketing*, 55 (April), 29-37.

Kalwani, Manohar U. and Narakesari Narayandas (1995) Long-Term Manufacturer-Supplier Relationships: Do They Pay Off For Supplier Firms? *Journal of Marketing*, 59 (1).

Kotha, Suresh (1997) Competing on the Internet: The Case of Amazon.com, *European Journal of Management*, in press.

Malone, T. W., J. Yates and R. I. Benjamin (1987) Electronic Markets and Electronic Hierarchies, *Communications of the ACM*, 30 (6), 484-497.

Mehta, Raj, Rajdeep Grewal and Eugene Sivadas (1996) International Direct Marketing on the Internet: Do Internet Users Form a Global Segment? *Journal of Direct Marketing*, 10 (Winter), 45-58.

Morgan, Robert M. and Shelby D. Hunt (1994) The Commitment-Trust Theory of Relationship Marketing, *Journal of Marketing*, 58 (July), 20-38.

Plummer, Joseph T. 1986) The Role of Copy Research in Multinational Advertising, *Journal of Advertising Research*, (October/November), 11-15.

Poon, S. and C. Jevons (1997) Internet-Enabled International Marketing: A Small Business Perspective, *Journal of Marketing Management*, 13, 29-41.

Quelch, John A.and Lisa R. Klein (1996) The Internet and International Marketing, *Sloan Management Review*, 37 (Spring), 60-75.

Rayport, Jeffrey F and John J. Sviokla (1994) Exploiting the Virtual Value Chain, *Harvard Business Review*, 73 (6), 75-85.

Samiee, Saeed (1998) Exporting and the Internet: a conceptual perspective, *International Marketing Review*, 15 (5), 413-426

Chapter 13

ONLINE SELLING STRATEGIES

LEARNING OBJECTIVES

1. Learn about virtual segments, frictionless transactions, and information intermediaries and how these factors will impact competition.
2. Consider how firms will compete using searchable hypertext.
3. Anticipate trends toward disintermediation and toward new types of intermediation.

For business, there is good news and bad news about selling over the Internet. The good news is that anybody can do it, and the bad news is that anybody can do it. Compared to other forms of selling, there are only modest barriers to starting an Internet selling business. Large numbers of businesses, large and small, have jumped in to try their hand at online selling. Every year it becomes easier and cheaper for businesses to create Web sites and sell via the Internet. As a result, we can expect to see a more crowded marketspace with firms grasping at anything that might allow themselves to better compete. The purpose of this chapter is to discuss some of the trends that will affect this competition.

One classic marketing strategy is to create a unique product or service to attract a certain group of consumers with similar tastes. A group of consumers that reacts to a marketing program the same way is called a segment; a small segment usually is called a niche. When the target niche of consumers is scattered all over the country, or all over the world, it can be very expensive to reach the individuals comprising that niche. Once Alice B. Toklas described Oakland, California by saying that, "There is no there, there." The same can be said of the Internet—there is no "there," there because the Internet makes customer geography largely irrelevant. You can target **virtual segments** of consumers who do not live anywhere near each other. The lack of physical proximity is no handicap in the electronic sphere where you can inexpensively reach, and provide service for, people all over the world.

Consider the market for so-called cult movie "classics" produced by the director Ed Wood. This is not exactly a mass market. In fact, as with most of the movies in this genre, people stayed away from the theaters in droves. However, a company like "Ronnie Cramer's Cult Film Site" (http://sepnet.com/rcramer/) can sell to individuals anywhere who, for whatever reason, want to buy videos of some of these films.

We should not conclude from the above discussion of virtual segments that the Internet has made geography wholly irrelevant. In fact, the choice of physical location can be very important for a Web-based retailer. Creating a selling site that relies on Internet technology is best done in places where it is possible to attract talented employees, often where there is already a critical mass of technology workers. In addition, the process of order fulfillment must be thoughtfully planned out with special attention paid to questions of warehouse location, shipping facilities, and other transportation considerations. Of course, favorable tax laws can also help.

One important trend furthered by the Internet is a change toward compressed marketing channels and **disintermediation.** Many consumer products go through a variety of intermediaries after they leave the manufacturing plant and before they wind up in the hands of consumers. On the Internet, firms do not need to be part of an elaborate channel of such intermediaries. Instead, they can speak directly to consumers, bypass retailers or other middlemen, and thereby reduce transaction costs. In addition, shorter channels provide an opportunity for faster delivery.

The possibility of disintermediation does not necessarily imply that today's retail powers will simply roll over and die. While many retailers from discounters, to category killers through department stores and supermarkets, have not yet come to terms with the Internet, it is likely that eventually companies that own such stores will be able to create a certain synergy between an online presence and their physical assets. For example, it would be possible to provide "to go" shopping services for busy consumers who might find it more convenient to choose groceries on the Web and run into the store just long enough to pick up the week's food, already pre-bagged and ready to be placed in the trunk. Clothing could be purchased online with the retailer taking delivery and then providing tailoring or other services. Consumers could make appointments over the Internet to meet with sales help at certain times of the day. Or a food retailer could alert you by email to sale items for your favorite style of ethnic food.

Although the Internet can be used to create a compressed channel, it is somewhat ironic that the Internet also offers the possibility of new forms of intermediation. Since the Internet will allow market channel members to more closely coordinate, it will facilitate the outsourcing of intermediary functions. This was discussed in the last chapter in the context of business-to-business marketing. On the consumer side, the Internet offers the possibility of new information channels and services including search, evaluation, best price available, needs assessment, product matching, return and warranty services, and many other services. Such services could be especially useful when the product has credence or experience characteristics that cannot be evaluated during an Internet search.

Consider two other possibilities for new information intermediaries: 1) Consumers could track their own purchase histories, or allow someone to do so, and then provide these histories to an intermediary who would then sell them to other firms possibly after deleting identifying information. The consumer would then receive a royalty when these data were used. 2) Consumers could be recruited into buyers clubs that would then serve as an intermediary, buying bulk purchases. **Virtual buying pools** have already created this kind of transaction aggregation in the automobile market. Indeed, as the Internet lowers barriers to entry and further internationalizes an already crowded marketspace, information intermediaries may well become indispensable, trusted third parties helpful to both buyers and sellers.

Online selling sites can be used to provide very efficient consumer searches. In effect, the sheer speed of network servers can be harnessed along with well crafted search algorithms so that consumers can find products that most closely match their tastes. A site can store customer information that can be used in later transactions to identify and display consideration sets most suited to the individual's taste, and to display information about attributes that the individual will likely be most concerned about.

A Web site can offer things that retailers cannot afford to keep in the store due to limited retail space. A Web site can even let you offer far more than can be shown in a catalog. As the coverage in a catalog increases, the catalog gets more bulky and hard to search, not to mention difficult to lug around from room to room. Hypertext allows most of the information to remain hidden until the consumer calls for it specifically. A common technique is to provide a thumbnail picture of the item. The consumer does not have to look at the large picture of the item unless he wants to, in which case he clicks on the thumbnail and views the bigger version of the image. Such techniques allow retailers to have a huge number of items for sale online and to offer thorough information about each offered item. A computer database can grow without limit, assuming high-quality searching tools that allow the consumer to search on attributes, prices, or brands, as needed.

Another important benefit of hypertext is its ability to present assortments of complementary merchandise. You can cross-link items such as plane tickets and luggage, recipes and ingredients, shirts and ties, stationary and pens, or greeting cards and gift ideas.

Unfortunately, the quality of the online experience is not as good as that with a paper catalog. Common household modems and the current capability of computer monitors severely restrict the quality of presentation possible on the Web. Compared to paper, an online retailer is limited to low-quality graphics and text. This restriction could make for a less-than-compelling shopping experience. Only the most creative page designers can get around the limitations of today's Web. In this respect, a well-crafted page fills the same kind of role played by store atmosphere or store image.

An online retailer needs to provide motivation to purchase now, online, instead of later at a store. But fortunately, the Internet has a flexibility advantage over print media, and to a certain extent over broadcast media. You should use this flexibility to create the impression of timeliness. Anyone with a little knowledge of HTML, or access to an HTML editor, can change things on the Internet at any time. The server housing the selling site can be programmed to automatically change things day by day or even hour by hour. You should have a healthy amount of bargains, closeout specials, this-week-only deals (or day or hour), prominently featured among your offerings.

You need to make sure the buying process is easy. Make sure your selling site is easy to navigate and easy to figure out how to buy. Just as in offline transactions, the consumer needs to be able to keep track of what they have bought so far. Many sites use a shopping basket metaphor to make buying easier. And whenever the user makes a choice, there should be confirmation or feedback for their purchase.

Costs and Prices

Online selling is highly automated, and electronic payment standards may make it even more efficient. Automation lowers transaction costs toward the goal of purely frictionless transactions. Friction is a term used to describe the overhead involved in processing a transaction. Since labor tends to be a large expense for most products and services, reducing the amount of labor required to sell an item goes a long way in removing this friction. In online selling, the consumer takes on more of the work, filling out online forms, searching without a salesperson present, typing in her own credit card number, and confirming the order. Firms that can lower their overhead and transaction costs while still managing to add value to the buying experience using search and other hypertext capabilities will prosper.

Compared to other forms of direct marketing, the Internet realizes the following cost advantages:

Transaction Automation: Using computers and software reduces the need for human sales staff as is required when the phone is used. Nor is a sales force needed to get orders as is the case with push telemarketing. In fact, automatic electronic payment mechanisms can reduce the human intervention needed below that of direct mail. Having said that, it can difficult to know how much is actually being saved since it may not be clear whether the company Web site is generating new sales or merely substituting for a toll-free number or other channel.

Reduced Cost Per Piece: In economic terms, the cost function for electronic communication with customers is very flat with little or zero marginal cost compared to other forms of direct marketing such as direct mail.

Why? Each catalog you mail requires a postage payment, an envelope and a printed catalog. The price of mailing the 1,001st catalog is only a little bit less, or even the same, as the price of mailing the first one. When we compare this to computer-mediated selling, we find that the 1,001st customer to arrive at a Web site adds only an infinitesimal cost to the firm.

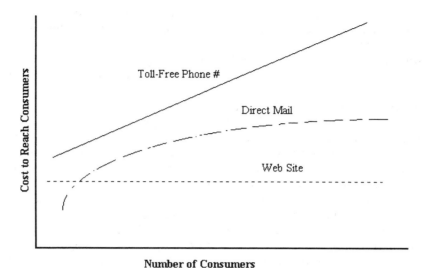

Cost to Reach Consumers

Toll-Free Phone #

Direct Mail

Web Site

Number of Consumers

Figure 13.1

As the number of customers rises, the cost of sending them mail or talking to them on the phone also rises. With the Interrnet, you pay a fixed start-up cost for your hardware and your network connection, but then your costs basically stay flat regardless of how many consumers visit your site.

Automated Post Purchase Support: The Internet can be used to provide usage hints, help, fixes, information about delivery, and other things usually done more expensively with a toll-free phone number.

The above cost-reducing factors suggest that the Internet might well represent a force to reduce prices in many markets. Further, the ease with which sellers can put a site on the Internet could produce something that resembles what economists call **pure competition**. Pure competition is characterized by very narrow price differences from one competitor to another even if they are in different nations. After all, why should a consumer who can effortlessly search for the cheapest product pay any more than the lowest price available on the entire Internet? Following this logic one step further, all firms would have to match the lowest firm's prices just to stay in business. And as mentioned earlier in the chapter, there is nothing to prevent consumers from organizing into virtual buying pools or cooperatives that demand even lower prices due to the volume of purchases they make for their members.

These price suppressing mechanisms might be ameliorated, however, by the following factors:

Price Tuning: Price can be customized automatically by electronic commerce software based on the geographical location of the buyer, their previous purchase history at the site, and other factors captured from them upon their first purchase. Such adaptive pricing could allow the seller to receive the highest amount possible on an individual customer basis. In addition, monitoring of global competitive and environmental factors could allow rapid minute-to-minute changes in prices.

Specialization: Firms can afford to offer a wider variety of niche or specialty products on the Internet not available through other channels. This might allow higher prices.

Superior Service: On the Internet, just as in the offline world, firms will be able to charge a premium for doing a better job at providing what consumers really want. The online world will offer many powerful ways to add value to the purchase of a good or service. Many of these techniques were discussed in Chapter 6, and they center on creating a relationship with the consumer. This could entail anything from timely email notification of bargains, to free samples, contests, and of course content provided by the community of others interested in your particular product category. Certainly the concept of service implies the timely response to consumer email queries, and convenient order fulfillment.

Although selling on the Internet can open up cost advantages for an online business, running a Web site is not free. There are four types of cost involved: hardware, software, telecommunications, and other services. Some typical items are given below:

Hardware: Servers, backup equipment, uninterruptible power supply, clients used for development, network hubs and routers, scanner, printer, firewall.

Software: Web server software, photo editing software, HTML or page editor, firewall software.

Telecommunications: Domain name, connectivity, and bandwidth.

Other Services: Page and site design, keeping the site fresh and well maintained, order fulfillment, CGI programming.

Summary

1. The Internet is creating certain trends, and accelerating others, such as virtual segments, disintermediation, frictionless transactions, and information intermediaries.
2. Firms will compete using the quality of the interactive experience. Search capabilities, talented visual artists, hypertext specialists, and other computer specialists will help firms stand out from the numerous competitors in the marketspace.

Online Activities

Visit the companion Web site at www.wiley.com/college/hofacker for chapter summaries, examples, hypertext cases, homework assignments, text material updates, research exercises, and *Wall Street Journal Interactive Edition* access.

GO TO   http://www.wiley.com/college/hofacker

THE WALL STREET JOURNAL.

References

Alba, Joseph, Lohn Lynch, Barton Weitz, Chris Janiszewski, Richard Lutz, Alan Sawyer and Stacy Wood (1997) Interactive Home Shopping: Consumer, Retailer, and Manufacturer Incentives to Participate in Electronic Marketplaces, *Journal of Marketing*, 61 (July), 38-53.

Bailey, J. P. and J. Y. Bakos (1997) An Exploratory Study of the Emerging Role of Electronic Intermediaries, *International Journal of Electronic Commerce*, 1 (Spring).

Bakos, Yannis (1997) Reducing Buyer Search Costs: Implications for Electronic Marketplaces," *Management Science*, 43 (12), 1676-1692.

Burke, Ray (1996) Virtual Shopping: Breakthrough in Marketing Research," *Harvard Business Review*, 74 (March/April), 120-131.

Burke RR (1997) Do you see what I see? The future of virtual shopping, *Journal of the Academy of Market Science*, 25 (4), 352-360.

Butler, Patrick and Joe Peppard (1998) Consumer Purchasing on the Internet: Processes and Prospects, *European Management Journal,* 16 (5), 600-610.

Dabholhar, P. (1994) Technology Based Service Delivery, *Advances in Services Marketing and Management*, 3, 241-271.

Doherty, N. F., F. Ellis-Chadwick, and C. A. Hart (1998) The Commercialisation of the Internet: A Study of the Devlopment and Utilisation of the World Wide Web in the UK Retail Sector, Working Paper, Loughborough University.

File, Karen Maru. and Russ Alan Prince (1993) Evaluating the Effectiveness of Interactive Marketing, *Journal of Services Marketing*, 7 (3), 49-58.

Holland, Christopher P. and Geoffrey A. Lockett (1992) IT Strategy in Retailing: Organizational Change and Future Direction, *Journal of Strategic Information Systems*, 1 (June), 134-141.

Keeney, Ralph L. (1999) The Value of Internet Commerce to the Customer, *Management Science,* 45 (April), 533-542.

Mata, F. J., W. L. Ruerst and J. B. Barney (1995) Information Technology and Sustained Competitive Advantage, *MIS Quarterly*, 19 (4), 487-505.

O'Connor, Gena C. and Robert M. O'Keefe (1997) Viewing the Web as a Marketplace - the Case of Small Companies, *Decision Support Systems*, 21 (3), 171-183.

O'Keefe, Robert M., Gina C. O'Connor and Hsiang-Jui Kung (1998) Early Adopters of the Web as a Retail Medium: Small Company Winners and Losers, *European Journal of Marketing*, 32 (7/8), 629-643.

Peterson, Robert A., Sridhar Balasubramanian and Bart J. Bronnenberg (1997) The Implications of the Internet for Consumer Marketing, *Journal of the Academy of Marketing Science*, 25 (Fall), 329-346.

Sarkar, M, B. Butler, and C. Steinfeld (1998) Cybermediaries in Electronic Marketspace - Toward Theory Building, *Journal of Business Research,* 41 (3), 215-221.

Spiller, Peter and Gerald L. Lohse, (1998) A Classification of Internet Retail Stores, *International Journal of Electronic Commerce*, 2 (2), 29-56.

Tiwana, A.B. (1998) Interdependency Factors Influencing the World Wide Web As a Channel of Interactive Marketing, *Journal of Retailing and Consumer Services*, 5 (October), 245-253.

Whinston, Andrew B., Dale O. Stahl and Soon-Yong Choi (1997) *The Economics of Electronic Commerce.* Indianapolis, IN: Macmillan Publishing Company.

Weiber, Rolf and Tobias Kollmann (1998) Competitive Advantages in Virtual Markets - Perspectives of "Information-Based Marketing" in Cyberspace", *European Journal of Marketing*, 32 (7/8), 603-615.

Chapter 14

THE MECHANICS OF ELECTRONIC COMMERCE

LEARNING OBJECTIVES

1. Learn about interactive forms that allow consumers to enter their requests.
2. Learn how merchants collect money over the Internet.
3. Discover some of the ways that unscrupulous computer users can break into other systems.
4. Learn how to protect your business and customers from break-ins. Understand the fundamentals of public key cryptography.

The act of purchase is usually precipitated by an intention to buy on the part of the consumer. Unfortunately, after the consumer has decided to buy, but before the transaction has actually been executed, there is a brief moment in which it is still possible to lose the sale. Various situational factors, such as the buyer's mood and things she sees right at the time she is about to buy, can still influence her. Therefore, the specific mechanism used to capture the sale can be very important to the profitability of online commerce. It is those details that constitute the main topic of this chapter.

A well-designed interactive form allows the online purchase to be quick and simple. There are usually two stages to the online purchase. First, the consumer must specify what she wants to buy. Second, she must enter payment information. With the first step, the selling site should make it easy on the buyer to indicate what she wants, and she certainly shouldn't have to remember or write down what she has chosen. A site should record the specific item and quantity information a customer has entered and store it indefinitely until the customer is ready to make the payment. This is not as easy as it sounds since the hypertext transfer protocol used by the Web does not really "connect" the Web visitor to the Web site. What this means is that the Web server does not keep track of whether it has already sent a page to someone requesting another page. Software used to record what a visitor has bought must be purchased separately or built using the techniques described in the HTML sidebar in this chapter.

Many sites use a "shopping basket" metaphor in which a button appears besides each item; specifying a quantity and clicking the button causes the quantity and item to be stored—added to the basket until payment. When the customer presses the button to prompt payment for the items she has chosen, the site should

HTML Sidebar

Receiving input from Web visitors is achieved using two types of software. First, HTML is used to create a Web page known as a form. A form is just like any other Web page, except that it contains input fields that allow the visitor to enter information. Input fields are created with the <input> markup. For example, to create a simple blank space for the consumer to type in an address, you would use the following markup:

```
<input       type=text
name="Address" size=37>
```

Another important markup used for forms is the appropriately named <form> markup. A <form> markup begins a form and a </form> markup ends a form. An example appears below.

```
<form
action="script.cgi">
```

The action parameter specifies the name of the computer program that will read the information the consumer has provided, perhaps perform some sort of action using this information, and create a new page based on the action. In the example above, the name of the computer program is *script.cgi*. Anything that script.cgi writes becomes part of the page that the consumer will see next. The phrase used to describe this technique is that script.cgi will create a new page **on the fly**.

---

summarize everything she has put in her basket, including totals and subtotals for multiple quantities of the same item. The shipping policy and charges, and any shipping options, should be presented as well. One useful strategy, if appropriate, is to explicitly include a "Web purchase discount" in all prices and totals, providing a reason for the customer to pay a repeat visit to your Web shop.

Payment Mechanisms

There are three basic ways to execute online transactions. Perhaps the simplest is to have customers create a house account with you. This solution likely eliminates the possibility of a quick impulse purchase, unfortunately. It is also somewhat labor intensive as someone at the selling firm must set up each customer's account.

A second method is to simply ask for billing information at the time of purchase using a standard HTML form. Some server-browser combinations allow forms to be encrypted for security. In addition, there are many firms that offer online credit card execution for a percentage of the sale.

Finally, there is the possibility of using "digital cash." In this approach, the customer can be completely anonymous, just as with real cash. Digital cash works something like a debit card; a customer prepays to be able to spend a certain amount of money online.

Online transactions are likely to become even more efficient in the future. Whenever you use a credit card now, your 16-digit credit card number must be checked to see if it is valid, the price of the item or service must be checked to see if it will exceed your credit limit, a bill must be prepared and mailed to you, and the amount of your check to the credit card company must be entered and subtracted from your account. Credit card companies generally charge merchants 2 percent of the transaction amount to pay for all this service. As the online purchasing process becomes more and more automated, however, we might expect the economy at large to become even more efficient. This would also pave the way for **microtransactions**, in which the consumer might be charged a fraction of a penny to see a certain page or to hear a certain song.

Network Security and Cryptography

Security on the Internet works something like this old joke:

> Once there were two hunters in the deep forest. They had gone down to a nearby lake for some water, leaving their guns back at the campfire. A grizzly bear approached them rapidly, and after a frightening chase, fortunately the bear went on its way. Back at the camp, the first hunter asked the second hunter, "Why did you run? You know you can't outrun a grizzly." His friend replied, "I didn't need to outrun the grizzly; I just needed to outrun you."

The analogy to Internet security is that if someone wants to break into your system badly enough, he probably can. The key is to make it difficult enough that he chooses to go after someone else's system.

Techniques Used by Crackers

The term "hacker" is often used to refer to someone who breaks into computer systems. This usage is actually incorrect. Hacking means modifying a computer program, while cracking is breaking into computer systems. People who do this have a variety of diabolical, albeit creative, techniques to break into places they shouldn't. Of course you should be aware that it is against the law to break into a computer system without permission, and if your system is violated, the appropriate law enforcement authorities should be called. Here are some of the most common techniques:

Inside job: Most computer security violations result from nontechnical problems, such as a clerk who gives out a password to a stranger on the phone or a disgruntled worker intent on sabotage.

Password guessing: Potential intruders can use a computer attached to the Internet to try to log on to an account on your server trying various passwords. If just one employee has a simple password, you could be out of luck. We discuss exactly what constitutes a good password below.

Packet sniffing: Crackers sometimes capture packets of data from a segment of wire or fiber and look them over for signs of a password or credit card number.

Keyboard sniffing: This technique entails using a virus program to capture keystrokes on someone's machine. The captured information is then encrypted and posted by the virus to a Usenet newsgroup for later retrieval by the computer criminal.

IP Spoofing: This technique involves a cracker pretending that his or her packets are coming from a trusted network address. In general, computer scientists use the verb "spoof" to refer to pretending to be someone or something that you are not.

Race condition: Here the crackers race to beat some information requested by a client from the server, so that they can pretend to be the server. And then when the "server" asks you for your password, you end up typing it for the crackers, not the real server.

Session hijacking: An Internet service called **telnet** is often used to access a larger computer from a PC or Mac. It is possible to talk over telnet sessions from afar and then control what gets typed in, for example a request to change the password. Unbeknownst to you, the thieves then type in a new password "on your behalf."

Defenses Used

On the other side of the fence, legitimate computer users have come up with techniques that can foil these kinds of attacks. The first line of defense is relatively low-tech: making sure that everyone has a good password and changes that password frequently. The definition of a good password is a password that is hard to guess. The longer a password is, and the more types of characters you use, the harder it is to guess. Consider what would happen if you restricted yourself to three upper case letters. In that case there are only 26 x 26 x 26 (26^3) or 17,576 combinations that a thief would have to run through in order to hit your password. In fact, on average he would have to run through only half of these combinations to guess your password. A computer program could go through all 17,576 combinations rather quickly, trying to log on as you, by seeing which of the 17,576 combinations work. On the other hand, say you have an eight-character password instead of a three-character code. Let's also say you use upper and lower case (52 total possible characters), plus any of the keyboard numerals (10 more characters) or any of the 32 special characters on the keyboard. In that case you would have 93^8 combinations, a monstrous number that would likely foil any attempt to guess your password.

Your password also becomes easy to guess if you use your name, phone number, address or anything else that might be familiar. Actually, it is a bad idea to use any string of letters that is a word in any of the world's languages. Crackers can convert dictionaries into passwords, and then cross-check your password against the converted words to look for matches.

Another important defensive technique is the **firewall**. A firewall is a computer system that sits between the server and the rest of the Internet. The firewall system decides what kinds of packets are allowed to pass between the selling site and the outside world. For example, if nobody from the outside is allowed to telnet to the server, then packets that are part of a telnet session are simply filtered out of the bitstream.

Secure Transactions

In addition to the basic security methods described above, there are other ways of protecting customer data produced as a result of transactions. The simplest approach to security is often a low-tech solution. For example, a merchant might require that customers use the phone to set up a house account the first time they buy something from them. In a phone conversation, a merchant can obtain a customer's credit card number and shipping address, and both can be stored offline, on a computer not connected to the Internet. As a matter of policy, the shipping address associated with the customer's account might not be changed without some kind of verification, again via a telephone call. Goods purchased with stolen account information could then not be redirected to a different location.

To execute transactions purely online, on the other hand, requires that the consumer type credit card and shipping information into the browser at least once. Three new advances in technology make this process safer. First, an initiative by MasterCard, Visa, IBM, Netscape, and Microsoft, called the Secure Electronic Transaction or **SET**, makes the transaction so secret that the credit card number is hidden even from the merchant! Second, there is the possibility of using "digital cash," as described earlier in this chapter. In this approach, the spender can be completely anonymous, just as with real cash. A third approach, which is being widely implemented at this time, is called **public key cryptography,** discussed in detail in the following section.

Public Key Cryptography

For ages, people have invented ways of sending secret messages to each other, but these methods generally require that the communicating parties first exchange some kind of key in private. But what do two people do if their only communication channel is insecure? What if they are getting together for the first time over the Internet, which as we have seen in the previous section, is an admittedly insecure communications channel? How can they share a key which will enable them to exchange messages secretly? Presumably if they could send the key safely they wouldn't need to encrypt their transactions in the first place!

The solution to this dilemma is provided by a mathematical technique that creates keys in pairs. Each user obtains both a private key and a public key. What the **private key** encrypts, only the **public key** can decrypt. What the public key encrypts, only the private key can decrypt.

The relationship between the two keys allows a person to share his public key even over an insecure network like the Internet, as long as his private key remains secret. The ability to send the public key to anyone without fear creates two useful byproducts: **Confidentiality** and **authentication.**

Confidentiality is the ability to send a secret message to someone without fear that it will be intercepted and understood by anyone else. To send a secret message to you, I would use your public key to encrypt the message. Only you can decrypt the message, using your private key. The latest versions of popular Web browsers have this technology programmed into them. When a consumer needs to make a confidential transaction such as typing their credit card number into a form, the server for the selling site can create a public and private key pair. The server then sends the public key to the consumer's browser. The public key is used by the browser to encrypt the information that has been typed into the form, including the credit card number. Only the server can decrypt this message since only the server has access to the private key that it had created just moments before. The pair of keys is then discarded after the transaction.

Authentication is the ability to demonstrate that you are who you say you are. Authentication also uses a private and public key pair. Let's say you want to send someone a message and the recipient needs to be confident that the message indeed came from you. In this case, you use your private key to encrypt something, perhaps an add-on to your message including your name, the date, and the number of characters in the message. You then add this encrypted information to the end of the message as a **digital signature**. Anyone can verify that you sent the message because your public key, and no one else's, will be able to decrypt the digital signature.

Public key cryptography can be used not only in the transmission of sensitive data, but also in the storage of it. You can encrypt a disk file containing credit card numbers and then decrypt it only when you need to look up someone's information. The only down side to this little piece of mathematical wizardry is the realization that terrorists and other bad guys can use it also to hatch their plans in secret. The various ethical dilemmas posed by the Internet and its technology will be discussed in Chapter 17.

Summary

1. An HTML form is the way that consumers indicate their online choices.
2. A variety of payment mechanisms have been proposed for the Internet including SET, digital cash, and standard browser-server interaction encrypted with public key cryptography.
3. Individuals sometimes try to break into computers using a variety of techniques such as IP spoofing, race conditions, sniffing, and password guessing.
4. A firm can protect itself by requiring complex passwords for all staff, using a firewall and implementing encryption.

Online Activities

Visit the companion Web site at www.wiley.com/college/hofacker for chapter summaries, examples, hypertext cases, homework assignments, text material updates, research exercises, and *Wall Street Journal Interactive Edition* access.

GO TO | http://www.wiley.com/college/hofacker

THE WALL STREET JOURNAL.

References

Beth, Thomas (1995) Confidential Communication on the Internet, *Scientific American*, (December), 88-91.

Carroll, Michael (1998) Business-to-Business E-Commerce, *Web Techniques*, 3 (November), 44-52.

Jones, Russ (1998) Small Change, *Web Techniques*, 3 (August), 51-56.

Nath, R. M., K. Akmanligil, and K. Hjelm (1998) Electronic Commerce and the Internet: Issues, Problems, and Perspectives, *International Journal of Information Management,* 18 (2), 91-101.

Nolan, Godfrey (1998) Virtual Credit, *Web Techniques*, 3 (August), 43-49.

Stein, Lincoln D. (1998) SET - Who Needs It?, *Web Techniques*, 3 (August), 10-14.

Part IV
PROVIDING WEB CONTENT

Chapter 15

THE CONTENT SITE VISITOR

LEARNING OBJECTIVES

1. Investigate the psychological construct called flow.
2. Compare and understand the differences between hedonic surfers and utilitarian searchers.

A content site generates revenue by getting people on the site, by having them look at a lot of pages on the site, and by getting them to come back to the site often. How do we do this? At one level, the simple answer is that you should make the site "interesting," "beneficial," "entertaining," or "fun." But what do these terms really mean? In this chapter we make these concepts more concrete, and also discuss the two basic segments of Web visitors: hedonic surfers and utilitarian searchers. Both groups are looking for interesting sites, but what each considers interesting varies.

Flow

Psychologists who have studied enjoyment have invented the concept of **flow** to try to capture what the enjoyment experience entails. Here is the definition of flow:

> Flow is an optimal psychological experience occurring when there is a match between the challenge at hand and one's skills.

Hitting that perfect match requires that the content site marketer understand the abilities of the target audience very well. In either case, if the challenges are too great for the skills, the visitor becomes frustrated and feels annoyance toward the site and the company. Conversely, if the challenges are too easy, the consumer gets bored and just leaves. But hit just the right amount of challenge and the consumer is in the "flow zone."

When consumers are in this flow zone, they feel a sense of playfulness. The word "optimal" in our definition implies that the Web visitor is having a peak experience. There is a feeling of being in control with highly focused attention and concentration. This sense of control is easier to achieve on the Internet, which after all is user driven, than with other media. Often there is a distorted sense of how much time was spent on the activity. When you are in this zone, you tend to enjoy the activity for its own sake, even though it might be part of some larger goal. The means become an end in themselves.

If you are able to induce this state in visitors, your company can reap rich rewards. There will be an increase in consumer learning about the site and about your firm, and increased memory recall for this learned information. In addition, the visitor will engage in more exploration and participation. Generally speaking, interacting with other visitors can increase flow, and increasing flow can cause an increase in interaction. A good site then creates a feedback mechanism that produces a positive subjective experience, a favorable attitude, and therefore a visitor likely to stay longer, return to the site, and to tell others what a great site it is. This last effect can increase the total visitors and enhance the site reputation, a phenomenon we might call "word of mouse."

Hedonic Surfers and Utilitarian Searchers

It is useful to make a distinction between two categories of Web site visitors. The first segment can be called **hedonic surfers.** Surfers are consuming a Web site by experiencing it in a way similar to how they would consume movies or sporting events. Often there is a strong nonverbal aspect to the hedonic experience, with images being quite important. The vividness of the online experience is especially important to surfers, and interaction with others can be highly rewarding to them. Services like **MUD**s (Multi User "Dungeons," a name inspired by the Dungeons and Dragons game), in which visitors engage in symbolic interaction with each other, and "try on" various identities or roles have been found to be literally addictive in their ability to keep surfers at a site.

The browsing of the surfer is spontaneous, that is, without a plan. The goal is escapist, to become immersed in the site, to experience a high degree of personal enjoyment either through arousal or pleasure or both. These undirected hedonic surfers are motivated to gather interesting and exciting experiences from the Web. The surfer judges potential clicks on a moment-to-moment basis to determine whether the new page will be fun and worth the wait during the loading time.

A unique site—one novel and interesting—works best for these surfers. It is possible that figuring out the design of the site could be part of the challenge that creates flow in the hedonic surfer. Often a **network design** of the information space will match the exploratory nature of surfing. In a network design, any page may be linked to any other page depending on the natural connections in the specific topic area covered by your site. And you get these folks to your site by pulling them in with links all over the Internet and ad banners on other sites.

If your Web content involves an opportunity to buy something, it is important to come up with strategies to sell to those who might just be surfing around, keeping their eyes open for a bargain for convenience or specialty goods. You might be able to offer a limited version of your real product for free. Software companies often use such a technique. Once a user becomes familiar with a product and comes to like it, the company then charges for an upgrade to the professional version. If you can think of a way to offer a low-cost trial, a contest, or a twist on the old "give the razor away for free but sell the razor blades" tactic, that would be an appropriate approach with these surfers. When some of your offerings represent a true bargain, and you change the specifics frequently, this keeps bargain hunters coming back to your site. On one of those visits, they may even turn from an idle surfer into a good customer spending serious money.

As noted, the second segment is comprised of **utilitarian searchers.** Their use of the Web is instrumental and rational. The Web is just an instrument allowing them to find the key piece of information they seek; they are applying logic to achieve a specific outcome. They are seeking something; they are really looking for some specific information. Since they have a goal, they have more of a work mentality. You can make the analogy that searchers act as if they are foraging for nuggets of food in an information forest. As a searcher comes upon a link, he or she must make a decision in the way a person might decide whether to climb a certain hill for some berries that might be at the top. If you decide correctly, you are rewarded at the top of the hill with some nutritious food. However if you decide wrongly, the calories you expend climbing the hill are not worth the calories you gather from the bushes at the top of the hill. Moment to moment, searchers are looking over the potential links on a page and deciding whether any of them are worth a click and the time it will take to load that next page. Will any of these links take them closer to that nugget of information they seek?

A well-organized and searchable site—one that lacks frivolous content and has a well-thought-out layout—works best for these seekers. Continuing the analogy of the hill and the berries, your site should be designed to quickly and correctly point them to the right "hill" for them, the one with the kind of berries they are seeking. Your information space should be organized logically, in a way that reflects the searcher's expectations. Of course, visitors will not be familiar with your organization's structure so you must meet their expectations, not yours.

For these visitors, the challenge that creates the flow state is already present in the content, in the information itself that they seek to find or understand at your site. The design of the site should not add to the challenge; the design should be transparent. In other words, the site itself should function so well and so naturally that the layout virtually disappears from the mind of the searcher, and instead the information sought takes center stage.

HTML Sidebar

You need to make sure your site is well represented in search engines to help folks find you. You can facilitate successful searches by putting keywords in the HTML <META> tag. The format appears as follows:

```
<META HTTP-
EQUIV="Keywords"
CONTENT="keyword1,
keyword2, ...">.
```

You would replace keyword1 with any terms you feel searchers would use to find you. It also helps to have a domain name that is logical and easy to guess and a simple URL. Your URL should not include a tilde (~), nor should it have any uppercase letters. It should be as short as possible.

Several models of Web design are emerging. One classic way of organizing a Web site is to utilize a hierarchy. A **hierarchical design** employs a tree structure, where the main page lists in a menu the various subpages, and each subpage in turn lists the various sub-subpages. But different types of information work best with different sorts of site structure. If you are presenting procedures or lists, a serial or **linear design** might work best. This kind of structure allows the visitor to view each page in a controlled sequence, with navigational aides allowing them to go to the next page, to the previous page, or back to the start. If you are presenting raw data, a **factorial design** or grid structure might be the best way to organize your information space. For example, if you are presenting a schedule, the visitor should be able to move from one hour to the next, but they should also be able to easily move from one day to the next. The schedule could be set up as a table, with rows, columns, or tiers representing the different categories for each piece of data. Finally, recall that for hedonic surfers, a network design where a page may be linked to any other page, is a possibility worth considering.

The Web Is a Niche Medium

At this point we should think a bit more about the visitor to a content site and how we should treat him or her. When there were a small number of media outlets, the goal was to create programming that appealed to as many visitors as possible. This is still the case with broadcast television and other forms of mass media. But the Web is not a mass medium, it is a niche medium. Its strength is in appealing to a small loyal audience characterized by a high level of repeat visits. Such an audience lets you charge a premium to certain advertisers who would love to reach your highly targeted visitors. The more narrow the audience, the more you can charge the right advertiser per impression or click-through.

The Web audience is extremely fragmented compared to the typical mass media audience. It is very difficult to achieve a large share, or even minimal awareness, with such a splintered audience. Consequently, well-known media brands such as ESPN's Sports Zone service (www.sportszone.com) Paramount's *Star Trek* franchise (www.startrek.com), or the Yahoo! index (www.yahoo.com) are very unusual, and certainly valuable. Yahoo! has used its brand equity wisely, leveraging its credibility to create a number of brand extensions including its Headlines service (dailynews.yahoo.com), Yahooligans for kids (www.yahooligans.com), and numerous regionally specific sites. But it may not be possible— or desirable in many cases—to attempt to reproduce the success of Yahoo. Instead you can use your own consistent design elements in your site to create a strong brand identity among a niche audience. Your visitors should be able to instantly recognize your site from any subpage. You should create a sense of style—perhaps a simple style if most of your visitors are utilitarian searchers, perhaps a more elaborate and artistic style if your visitors tend to be hedonic surfers—that uniquely identifies your content in the mind of the visitor.

Summary

1.   Flow is an optimal psychological experience occurring when there is a match between the challenge at hand and one's skills.
2.   There are two types of visitors to Web sites: those enjoying the surfing of the Web for its own sake and those searching for specific information. We call the first group hedonic surfers and the second group utilitarian searchers.

Online Activities

Visit the companion Web site at www.wiley.com/college/hofacker for chapter summaries, examples, hypertext cases, homework assignments, text material updates, research exercises, and *Wall Street Journal Interactive Edition* access.

GO TO   http://www.wiley.com/college/hofacker

 **THE WALL STREET JOURNAL.**

References

Babin, Barry J., William R. Darden and Mitch Griffin (1994) Work and/or Fun: Measuring Hedonic and Utilitarian Shopping Value, *Journal of Consumer Research*, 20 (March), 644-656.

Csikszentmihalyi, Mihaly and I. Csikszentmihalyi (Eds.), *Optimal Experience: Psychological Studies of Flow in Consciousness*, New York: Cambridge University Press.

Csikszentmihalyi, Mihaly (1990) *Flow: The Psychology of Optimal Experience*. NY: Harper and Row.

Davis, Fred D., Richard P. Bagozzi and Paul R. Warshaw (1992) Extrinsic and Intrinsic Motivation to Use Computers in the Workplace, *Journal of Applied Social Psychology*, 22 (July), 1111-1132.

Eliashberg, Jehoshua and Mahanbir S. Sawhney (1994) Modeling Goes to Hollywood: Predicting Individual Differences in Movie Enjoyment, *Management Science*, 40 (September), 1151-1173.

Fischer, E., J. Bristor, and B. Gainer (1996) Creating or Escaping Community? An Exploratory Study of Internet Consumers' Behaviors, in K.P. Corfman and J. Lynch (Eds.), *Advances in Consumer Research*, Provo, UT: Association for Consumer Research.

Ghani, Jawaid A. and Satish P. Deshpande (1994) Task Characteristics and the Experience of Optimal Flow in Human-Computer Interaction," *The Journal of Psychology*, 128(4), 381-391.

Gould, Stephen J. and Dawn B. Lerman (1998) Postmodern" versus "Longstanding" Cultural Narratives in Consumer Behavior: An Empirical Study of NetGirl Online, *European Journal of Marketing*, 32 (7/8), 644-654.

Hammond, K., G. McWilliam, and A. N. Diaz (1998) Fun and Work on the Web: Differences in attitudes between novices and experienced users, *Advances in Consumer Research,* 25, 372-378.

Hiltz, Starr Roxanne and Kenneth Johnson (1990) User Satisfaction With Computer-Mediated Communication Systems, *Management Science*, 36 (6), 739-764.

Hirschman, Elizabeth C. and Holbrook, Morris B. (1982) Hedonic Consumption: Emerging Concepts, Methods and Propositions, *Journal of Marketing*, 46 (Summer), 92-101.

Hoffman, Donna.L., Thomas.P. Novak, and Patrali Chatterjee (1995) Commercial Scenarios for the Web: Opportunities and Challenges," *Journal of Computer-Mediated Communication*, 1 (3).

Holdbrook, Morris B., Robert W. Chestnut, Terence A. Oliva and Eric A. Greenleaf (1984) Play as a Consumption Experience: The Roles of Emotions, Performance, and Personality in the Enjoyment of Games, *Journal of Consumer Research*, 11 (September), 728-739.

Holbrook, Morris B. and Elizabeth C. Hirschman (1982) The Experiential Aspects of Consumption: Consumer Fantasies, Feelings, and Fun, *Journal of Consumer Research*, 9 (September), 132-140.

Kay, Robin H. (1993) An Exploration of Theoretical and Practical Foundations for Assessing Attitudes Toward Computers: The Computer Attitude Measure (CAM), *Computers in Human Behavior*, 9, 371-386.

Murphy, Jamie (1999) Surfers and Searchers, *Cornell Hotel and Restaurant Administration Quarterly*, Vol 40 (2), pp. 84-95.

Novak, Thomas P., Donna L. Hoffman, and Yiu-Fai Yung (1999) Measuring the Flow Construct in Online Environments: A Structural Modeling Approach, Working Paper, http://www2000.ogsm.vanderbilt.edu/.

Pereira, Rex E. (1998) Influence of Choice Context on Consumer Decision Making in Electronic Commerce, In Celia. T. Romm and Fay Sudweeks (Eds.), *Doing Business Electronically: A Global Perspective of Electronic Commerce*, London: Springer-Verlag.

Pirolli, Peter and Stuart Card (1995) Information Foraging in Information Access Enviroments, *Proceedings of the ACM Special Interest Group in Computer-Human Interaction*.

Shih, Chuan-Fong (1998) Conceptualizing Consumer Experiences in Cyberspace, *European Journal of Marketing*, 32 (7/8), 655-663.

Steuer, Jonathan (1992) Defining Virtual Reality: Dimensions Determining Telepresence, *Journal of Communication*, 42 (Autumn), 73-93.

Tambyah, S. K. (1996) Life on the Net: The Reconstruction of Self and Community, in K.P. Corfman and J. Lynch (Eds.), *Advances in Consumer Research*, Provo, UT: Association for Consumer Research.

Trevino, Linda Klebe. and Jane Webster (1992) Flow in Computer-Mediated Communication, *Communication Research*, 19 (5), 539-573.

Turkle, Shelley (1995) *Life on the Screen: Identity in the Age of the Internet*, New York: Simon and Schuster.

Venkatesh, Alladi (1998) Cybermarketscapes and Consumer Freedoms and Identities, *European Journal of Marketing*, 32 (7/8), 664-676.

Webster, Jane, Linda Klebe Trevino, Lisa Ryan (1993) The Dimensionality and Correlates of Flow in Human Computer Interactions, *Computers in Human Behavior*, 9 (Winter), 411-426.

Chapter 16

STRATEGIES FOR PROVIDING CONTENT

LEARNING OBJECTIVES

1. Learn how to derive revenue from visitors to a content site.
2. Learn how to attract people to a site.
3. Learn how to retain visitors once they arrive.
4. Learn how to engender repeat visits to a site.

Where Does Revenue Come From?

Content Web sites provide interesting or useful information to visitors, but pure content sites need to derive revenue from these visitors to justify their existence. A content site can produce revenue either through sponsored advertising or some form of viewer fee. Advertising is by far the most common revenue model, and this chapter will focus on supporting a content site with advertising. However, viewer fees come in many forms and offer an alternative strategy. A **subscription** or **discount** is a form of viewer fee that is paid up front and which entitles the buyer to a certain number of sessions, pages, bytes, searches, or time on the site. The fee might entitle an individual, company, or department access to the content for a month or a year. Usage might be unlimited, or restricted and subject to add-on fees. Hoover's allows business researchers to access its data for a fee, Individual.com provides custom multimedia content to businesses, and *The Wall Street Journal* (www.wsj.com), charges a simple flat fee for a monthly subscription.

One dilemma that emerges from charging consumers before they visit a site is how to let them know the site is of high quality without giving away access to the site before the sale. An organization like *The Wall Street Journal* can rely on its print version to establish its reputation, but such an approach does not address the problem for Internet-only companies. Web-based companies can come up with creative solutions to this dilemma, perhaps by providing demo pages or trial access that lasts a specified amount of time. If the site offers some sort of service or problem solution, it might be able to provide an interactive problem that can be solved to demonstrate the ability of the site to do what it claims, as might be the case with financial calculator software.

A second type of viewer fee is one that is charged only after actual access. This **pay-per-view** revenue strategy requires the accumulation of **microtransactions**, which are exchanges involving very low prices for the right to see individual pages, or to issue certain commands. It is unknown at this time whether consumers will balk at having to make lots and lots of "microdecisions."

Unlike subscription services, which are prepaid, pay-per-view revenue strategies resemble advertising in one important way. Sites supported by advertising and those supported by pay-per-view, desire a steady stream of many visitors. For both of these cases, the revenue stream can be divided into three components: the number of first-time visitors (we can also call this trial, or reach), the number of pages accessed per visitor (site depth) and the number of repeat visitors (revisit or frequency). This breakdown of the revenue stream into these three pieces will be discussed later in the chapter. For now, we turn our attention to the details of how a content site sells advertising space. It turns out that deciding how many banners to sell and where to place them is a subtle decision.

It is important that ads be limited in size lest the host page really begin to bog down during loading. As discussed in the previous chapter, slow pages can have disastrous effects on the desirability of a site for both hedonic surfers and utilitarian searchers. But there are other, more subtle considerations. Some advertisers pay only by the click-through. In that case, the main site is getting paid to encourage viewers to leave the site! It would be as if a TV station were getting paid to encourage viewers to leave the room and go to the refrigerator. That is all well and good, but it could mean that the visitor will not return, and you could lose the possibility of gaining more revenue from that visitor. Similarly, if you put ad banners in a premier location on your site, they could take away attention from other links that you are interested in having people visit.

Including links to other sites raises a similar dilemma. It can be a great service to have a collection of links to other content sites that might compete with you. But do you offer the visitor an easy opportunity to leave your site and visit the sites of your competitors? If competing sites are in fact offering content that is different from yours, you could help each other by cross-linking to each other's Web sites. On the other hand, if you and your competitor offer essentially the same information, it would be foolish of you to point your visitors to the other site. The answer then depends on whether you are running an information commodity site or one that is unique in some important way. If your clientele consists chiefly of utilitarian searchers, and the reliability of the information is an issue for both you and your competitors, it can make sense to point to other sites since you are helping the visitor by giving them a larger sample to use to make a judgment. If reliability is not an issue, and other sites have roughly the same information as yours, it would not make sense to link to competitors.

We know that most Web sites create revenue by translating visitors into advertising exposures or clicks. Of course, the more people who look at or click on the ads placed on a content site, the higher the revenue to that site. As described above, logically there are three aspects to having more people available to look at or click on ads: getting people to visit the site, keeping them there looking at a lot of pages, and getting them to come back again later. Each of these aspects is now discussed in turn.

Getting People to Your Site

All new sites face the problem of attracting visitors. To solve this problem, it is important to not be biased against offline media. Traditional advertising, such as television, print, or outdoor, should be considered in a campaign to make a splash for a new site. Public relations can also help, but it is harder to create publicity for Web sites today than it was a few years ago. Not so long ago, having a Web site was in and of itself considered newsworthy. Now, it is harder to get coverage for a new site unless it is novel in some way. Nevertheless, the operator of a new site should try to get press attention by sending news releases to reporters about the nature of the site. These releases should stress the novel aspects of the site, and anything that it contains that would help the consumer.

Another basic and important technique is to register the site with various search engines. Most search engine sites have a mechanism in place to bring a new URL to the attention of the Webmaster. In some cases you may be able to purchase placement in the search list, either with an ad banner, or by simply having your site appear at the top of the output list, when visitors type in certain keywords. You should keep in mind that there are two different ways that consumers might find you on a search site. Some sites like Yahoo! have indices, or hierarchical lists that are categorized topically. Often consumers will work their way through these lists to find a category that interests them, so it is important that your site be present in the correct category when a consumer looks for your line of products. Submitting a URL to a site that has categorized lists requires that you carefully specify the lists you want to appear in, and that you follow up to make sure that your URL ends up in those lists. Another way that consumers search is by keyword. Sites such as AltaVista allow the consumer to quickly rummage through pages that contain certain looked-for words or phrases. Links are not particularly organized on a site like AltaVista. Instead, the designers of the search software attempt to discern what the consumer is really looking for, and to present the pages in order of likely relevance. Submitting a URL to a site like this tends to be much simpler. Be sure also to include important keywords on each of your pages and sub-pages. Also, the title of a page should be carefully thought out since titles are often heavily weighted by search software.

The Usenet newsgroup comp.www.announce exists and can also be used to announce new sites. Bring your site to the attention of other relevant sites so that you can garner as many links as possible.

Another way to announce a site is by buying ad banners or links on other sites. You may be able to do this fairly cheaply by trading links with other sites. Other techniques include partnering with established sites and either buying or trading with them.

Keeping People on Your Site

Once a visitor has arrived at your site, the goal of keeping him or her there in some large part depends on good site design, a topic to which we now turn. What we mean by "good" design can depend on the kinds of consumers that are visiting—surfers or searchers. But regardless of whether your visitors tend to be surfers or searchers, keep in mind that all Web users are impatient. The page has to load fast. Make sure you have sufficient bandwidth and computing power to handle all visitor requests. There are also important design choices that need to be made in terms of what images look like and how fast they load. Computer response time needs to be under one second to allow visitors to maintain the flow of thought. After 10 seconds, visitors completely lose focused attention. To keep loading time to under one second, assuming a 28.8 bit-per-second modem, requires that the entire page, including embedded graphics, be less than 3.6 kilobytes (K). To keep loading time to less than 10 seconds requires that the page be less than 36K. On a Windows system, you can check the size of files using the Windows Explorer program.

Solve the page size problem with creative design, not by using hard and simple rules about the size and number of images. While visitors will not stay long, or come back, if loading the site is interminable, a fast-loading but boring site with no pictures may not make a good impression either. That is where the creativity of a computer-savvy artist comes in. What's more, you can always break a page up into a series of smaller pages, with the main page having a link to each of the smaller pages. Further, the top of the each page should be designed so that there is something to read while the images are loading. The entry page of a site should be the fastest page to load and the top part of the entry page should be the fastest of all.

The more links there are on a page, the more opportunities there are for people to click. This will keep them on the site longer. But a certain proportion of users will not use the scroll bar. Try to keep links you want them to visit, or the attention grabbers, high enough on the screen so they don't need to use the scroll bar to see them.

People who read English and other languages written from left-to-right and top-to-bottom have a tendency to pay attention first to the upper left of the screen. Put important links there. In general, it is a good idea to make sure that all pages fit entirely, or nearly so, on one screen. For now, it is best to assume that most visitors are using no more than a 640 x 480 pixel window to view your site.

HTML Sidebar

You can speed the perception of the loading of a Web page by including the width= and height= subcommands of the <img> markup. The width= and height= parameters specify the image size, which allows the browser to set up the page even before the images have been retrieved. You can also use the alt= parameter to create text that will appear in place of the image. Finally, you can speed the loading of other pages by including trailing slashes for directories in the URLs for your links. For example, suppose that you want to create a link from a sub-page on your site to your main home page at www.mysite.com. You should specify the anchor markup for that link as <a href="http://www.mysite.com/">

Note the slash at the very end of the URL. Including that slash in your link will cause the home page to load more quickly since the server will know immediately a directory has been asked for, rather than a file.

Make sure there are text versions of all links. Because text loads faster than images, many searchers have "turned off" images in their browser. This means they will not see any of the instructions or words that appear in your images.

Each page should provide an easy way to get to other pages. For example, make sure each page has a clickable company logo at the top, or some other way to get to the main page. An ever present link to your main page makes it much easier for people to navigate your site. After all, you can't assume that all visitors land on the main home page first. Those linking in from search engines and other sites frequently arrive at your site on a minor page below the main one; make sure they can explore the rest of your pages effortlessly. And since many users prefer to use a search function to find things on a site, it's a good idea to include a search option on all pages.

If your site is organized in terms of hierarchical menus containing clickable bullet lists, each menu label has to be worth a click. The copy, or text, for each menu item should be bright. Phrases should have color, should grab the reader, but the copy should be brief. In this interactive medium, the visitor needs to be able to quickly grasp what is being presented and make a quick choice. Specific words work better than general concepts. To get them to click on one of your links, you need to provide a promise of some kind, a benefit. You need to stop readers in their tracks. The only way to do this is to create a high interest level, one that then must be backed up with an interesting payoff page for the link. While the transmission of information gets cheaper and cheaper, there is one aspect of the modern economy that is limited: The consumer has only so much time in the day and so much attention to pay. All content in all media competes for the sustained attention of today's audience. Ultimately, the profitability of content Web sites depends on audience members being loyal to your site.

Getting People to Return

In classic advertising terms, getting a large number of people to your site at least once is called "reach," but encouraging them to return increases "frequency." And how can you encourage return visits to your site? The main strategy used to encourage people to return to your site is fairly simple: Keep the content fresh. In order to generate repeat visits the site has to change frequently. And note well that there is nothing on the Web less fresh than a dead link that no longer works. Prune those links frequently! The ability to create quick changes is one of the hallmarks of the Internet medium. Try to highlight new material, provide an "article of the day," or a special with an expiration date. Tie pages to database information that is constantly updated. Of course, interactive aspects of the site should be presented early on. As in other media, the nature of the audience and their likes and dislikes must be thoroughly studied. Pay special attention to whether your audience is surfing or searching, and give them a reason to come back, again and again.

Summary

1.   Content sites generate revenue either by advertising, or some sort of viewer fee. Viewer fees can either be paid up front, or use some kind of pay-per-view formula.

2.   You can encourage first-time visits to your site using offline media and online links, especially links in traffic aggregation sites like search engines.

3.   The most important way to keep visitors on your site is to have fast-loading pages. A good navigational system is also necessary.

4.   Encourage revisits by constantly changing the content.

Online Activities

Visit the companion Web site at www.wiley.com/college/hofacker for chapter summaries, examples, hypertext cases, homework assignments, text material updates, research exercises, and *Wall Street Journal Interactive Edition* access.

GO TO   http://www.wiley.com/college/hofacker

References

Cahill, Dennis (1996) Further Issues in Pricing Strategies for Electronic Information, *Pricing Strategy and Practice*, 4 (1), 34-38.

Chyi, HI and G. Sylvie (1998) Competing with Whom, Where and How—A Structural Analysis of the Electronic Newspaper Market, *Journal of Media Economics*, 11 (2), 1-18.

Dellaert, Benedict, G.C. and Barbara E. Kahn (1999) How Tolerable is Delay: Consumers' Evaluations of Internet Web Sites after Waiting," *Journal of Interactive Marketing*, 13 (Winter), 41-54.

Evans, Philip B. and Thomas S. Wurster (1997) Strategy and the Economics of Information, *Harvard Business Review* (Sept-Oct), 70-83.

Freiden, Jon, Ronald Goldsmith, Scott Takacs and Charles Hofacker (1998) Information as a Product: Not Goods, Not Services, *Marketing Intelligence & Planning*, 16 (3), 210-220.

Held, R. and N. Durlach (1993) Telepresence, Time Delay and Adaption, in S. R. Ellis (1993*) Pictorial Communication in Virtual Communication in Virtual and Real Environments*, London: Taylor and Francis.

Lewis, Herschell Gordon and Robert D. Lewis (1997) *Selling on the Net*, Chicago NTC Business Books.

Meyer, Marc H, and Michael H. Zack (1996) The Design and Development of Information Products, *Sloan Management Review*, (Spring), 43-59.

Rowley, Jennifer (1995) Issues in Pricing Strategies for Electronic Information, *Pricing Strategy and Practice*, 3 (2), 4-13.

Schwartz, Evan I. (1997) *Webonomics*, New York: Broadway Books.

Sarvary, Miklos and Philip M. Parker (1997) Marketing Information: Competitive Analysis," *Marketing Science*, 16 (1), 24-38.

LEGAL AND ETHICAL ISSUES

1. Develop an understanding for the potential for controversy in Internet marketing.
2. Learn to routinely think about the problem of ethics in Internet Marketing.

Marketing Ethics

There are those who consider the phrase "marketing ethics" to be an oxymoron. But as we study marketing and the way it is evolving on this new medium, we should not become cynical. The decisions marketers make right now may well impact the way the Internet works for future generations.

Note that there are four possible frameworks for thinking about ethics. The **utilitarian approach** looks for the decision alternative that produces the greatest good for the greatest number of people.

The *prima facie* **duties framework** assumes there is a set of duties that constitute inherent moral obligations. Some duties include telling the truth, honoring contracts, maintaining obligations to partners or coworkers, ensuring that rewards and punishment are doled out according to merit, improving the happiness of others, and the duty not to injure others.

The **proportionality framework** considers the intention, the means, and the ends for a decision. Negative unintended consequences may be risked only if the means and ends are good, and there is a proportionate reason for taking the risk.

Finally, the **social justice framework** asks that we judge an action based on a neutral point of view, mentally avoiding any conflicts of interest by maintaining a strict attitude of justice.

Issues of Contention

The study of Internet marketing begs an examination of numerous issues of concern, from the privacy of consumer data to the use of keywords in the headers of Web pages. For many of these issues, there are more questions than answers.

Privacy—What kinds of information should be captured from users while they surf? Should information provided to a Web site be sold to other firms? Consumers' primary concern about providing personal data on Web sites is a fear that their data will be sold. **Cookies** raise privacy issues as well. The HTTP protocol does not keep track of who is making a connection. Each page request is treated as if it were an isolated incident. However, with cookies, the browser sends a message called a "cookie" to the server that the server can use to identify the visitor. Though the visitor has the option of turning cookies off, they are still not popular with many users because of privacy concerns. Despite these concerns, more and more companies are using cookies. The social justice framework would have us judge cookies not just from their use to our firm, but also from the point of view of the Web visitor. The benefit to us should not be the sole determining factor.

Copyright Law—A basic characteristic of digital information is the ease with which it can be copied. The intellectual property laws that govern ownership of information are different than the laws governing the ownership of physical things. The author of a digital work has the exclusive right to distribute copies of, or to modify, his or her work. In other words, the author of a text, piece of non-fiction, poem, or song, either online or offline, has a "copy right" that legally protects the author. To be specific, the author's economic interest is protected, not the work itself. Thus it is legal for someone to make fun of a piece of art and not be sued. The work itself is not literally protected. But keep in mind that to avoid copyright infringement, always make sure that copying a work does not lead to actual or potential market loss to the author. Others are allowed "fair use" for non-commercial purposes or for producing factual work as long as the copying does not impact the author's market potential. In this sense, the law takes a somewhat utilitarian approach. Companies, consumers, and others can use a work to everyone's benefit. Conversely, failing to allow someone to use your intellectual property even though your own economic interests would not be affected adversely would seem to be a selfish act if a greater good can be achieved through the fair use of the work. Before we leave this topic, it should be noted that the governments of the world do not always agree on copyrights, and in addition, this area tends to change from year to year as a result of local legislation.

Trademark Law—A related intellectual property concept is the notion of a trademark. A trademark is any word, name, or symbol used to identify a firm. Unlike copyright, which is an automatic protection, a trademark application must be submitted to the government. In the United States, the appropriate office is the United States Patent and Trademark Office. The Internet raises a number of trademark questions that a marketer might need to consider: Can I include a link to another company? Can I include that company's logo on that link? Can I borrow the logo, modify it as satire, and then publish the joke version? Can I copy another site? Can I put your company's name somewhere on my page so that when consumers use a search site to find your company, my company's page appears? The proportionality framework suggests that ethical use of another company's trademark depends on the intention of, or motivation for, that use, and the consequences to the other firm.

The Internet Name Space—To motivate this issue, consider how many cities have businesses with names such as "Main Street Electrical." How many businesses do you suppose are named "Western Hardware" or perhaps "Bay Rentals"? Sticking with the last example, which "Bay Rental" should legally be able to claim "www.bayrentals.com," one outside of Tampa, one in Wisconsin perhaps near Green Bay, or a Maryland company next to the Chesapeake? Of course, the current functioning of the domain name service, as described in Chapter 2, only allows one company to claim that URL, in this case a firm in San Jose, California. A simple application of the utilitarian approach might imply that bigger, better-known companies should have first priority to URLs. For example, what would have happened if a certain Horatio Z. McDonald claimed the mcdonalds.com domain before the food giant got around to it? In that case the millions of people looking for the famous restaurant would have had a hard time finding the Web page they had in mind. Perhaps the convenience of all these people should be taken into consideration. But some readers might not like stacking the deck even further in favor of bigger companies. Just as with the line in a fast food restaurant, some might lean toward a more objective rule, such as first come, first served. If Horatio reserved the name first, should it be his? We should note that some individuals, often known as cybersquatters, buy up domain names likely to be of interest to companies later. They then try to sell these names to companies at a profit. It is an important ethical and legal question as to whether this is a legitimate way to derive profits.

Unsolicited Commercial Email—Should spam be outlawed? Is it ethical? Often spammers disguise their email headers to appear as if the email has been sent from somewhere else. This would seem to be an important sign that even they do not believe what they are doing is ethical. Let's walk through a little mathematical argument from a utilitarian point of view. Suppose there are about 40 million businesses that you might possibly buy from on the Internet. In all likelihood, if anything, this is a gross underestimate. Now suppose that just 1/10th of 1 percent of them send you spam once per year. In that case, on average you would receive a bit more than 100 pieces of spam per day. Would your email account be useful under those circumstances? Sometimes spammers include a toll-free phone number in their message. I often call them and ask them about this. Generally speaking, the logic I get from them is that they "can't reach so many people so cheaply any other way." In other words, rather than evaluate the use of spam using the social justice framework, they only evaluate spam in terms of the benefit they receive.

Censorship—Should the government outlaw hate sites that try to push genocide or the overthrow of the government? And what of pornography? In the United States, there is a strong tradition of speech freedoms reinforced by the First Amendment of the Constitution. These freedoms are tempered in some cases by the rights of others. For example, TV stations are not allowed to broadcast sexually explicit material into people's homes without some sort of prior consent. Rules for magazines are much looser however. Magazines can and do provide this sort of material all of the time. So the question becomes, is the Internet more like TV or magazines?

In the United States, a court threw out what was called the "Computer Decency Act." Taking a utilitarian view, the judges ruled that even though the state has an interest in protecting children from certain kinds of materials, it is not right to ask millions of adults to forego these materials. Thus, reasoned the court, the state cannot force Internet communication down to a level appropriate for children.

The question of censorship becomes especially problematic in light of the fact that what is considered hateful or pornographic varies from one government to another. Does anyone doubt that what might be considered harmless fluff in Sweden could cause real consternation in Saudi Arabia? The ease with which the Internet allows international communication implies that the level of decency on the network may be determined by whatever country is the most lax. But does Saudi Arabia wish to let Sweden take away its power to control what its people see? Does it have any choice? This issue is related to the next topic as we will see below.

Long-Arm Jurisdiction—Whose laws should apply when a site in Aruba owned by an American is visited by online consumers from France? Recently, a Tennessee judge applied "local standards" to a sexually explicit Web site based in California. Here again the issue was what analogy to draw for the Internet? Is the Web site like a storefront that suddenly springs up in Tennessee when a visitor lands on the page? Or is it more like a magazine, arriving in a discrete brown wrapper in someone's mailbox? There is a long tradition of regulating the premises of "adult entertainment" retailing. There is just as long a tradition of tolerance for private consensual communication between adults. Which tradition should be applied to the Internet?

Gambling—www.interlotto.li is a Liechtenstein gambling site. Internet gambling may not be legal in the United States. This obviously poses a potential problem. Where is the gambling taking place? In the U.S. or in Liechtenstein?

Children's Issues—The FCC regulates children's TV programming to make sure that children are not deceived by advertising, but many toy, food, and clothing companies target their Web sites to children. Should the Internet be regulated in the same way that TV is?

Liquor—Until recently, hard liquor has not been advertised on TV in the United States, although it has been advertised in magazines. Should hard liquor be advertised on the Internet? Should cigarettes?

Cryptography—Should the government allow citizens to use **strong encryption** even though it could be used by terrorists or child pornographers? A phone conversation carried out over the Internet with encryption becomes, in effect, untappable. Here we must balance the potential harm against the utility of safe Internet transactions. And again, the choice of analogy we make certainly makes a difference. In particular, the U.S. government defines encryption to be like a munition, something rightfully controlled lest it fall into the wrong hands. In this view, using encryption software is like operating a potentially dangerous device or machine.

Civil libertarians, by comparison, think of encryption as speech. In their reasoning, a computer message is a form of speech consisting of a string of bits, and conversely, strings of bits passed from one person to another constitutes speech. The act of encryption is then not like using a munition, it is like talking—sending a key to someone is simply the act of sending them another string of bits. If the original string of bits is protected by the notion of free speech, why isn't the little string containing the key also protected? If we cannot impose a **prior restraint** on speech, why are we allowed to impose a prior restraint on speech about speech? That is what encryption is—speech about speech, in other words, some bits that are used to interpret another set of bits.

Sales Tax—If an online vendor sells to individuals from all over the world, and from all 50 of the United States, does the vendor have to take in sales tax? If so, is it an unreasonable burden on the vendor to learn the sales tax policies of all of these jurisdictions?

Summary

1.   There are four frameworks for marketing ethics: the utilitarian approach, the *prima facie* duties framework, the proportionality framework, and the social justice framework.

2.   The two types of laws regarding intellectual property are copyright laws and trademark laws.

3.   The Internet creates numerous problems in the area of privacy, long-arm jurisdiction, names, and children's issues.

Online Activities

Visit the companion Web site at www.wiley.com/college/hofacker for chapter summaries, examples, hypertext cases, homework assignments, text material updates, research exercises, and *Wall Street Journal Interactive Edition* access.

| GO TO | http://www.wiley.com/college/hofacker |

 THE WALL STREET JOURNAL.

References

Boehlefeld, Sharon Polancic (1996) Doing the Right Thing: Ethical Cyberspace Research," *The Information Society,* 12, 141-152.

Chonko, L.B., & Hunt, S.D. Ethics and marketing management: An empirical examination. *Journal of Business Research*, 1985, 13 (August), 339-359.

Cook, DL, and E. Coupey, (1998) Consumer Behavior and Unresolved Regulatory Issues in Electronic Marketing, *Journal Of Business Research*, 41 (3), 231-238.

Duncan, George T. (1996) Is My Research Ethical? *Communications of the ACM*, 39 (December), 67-68.

Foxman, Ellen R. and P. Kilcoyne (1993) Information Technology, Marketing Practice, and Consumer Privacy: Ethical Issues, *Journal of Public Policy and Marketing*, 12 (Spring), 149-166.

Komenar, Margo. *Electronic Marketing*, New York: John Wiley & Sons, Inc,. 90-98, 1997.

Laczniak, Gene R. (1983) Frameworks for Analyzing Marketing Ethics, *Journal of Macromarketing,* (Spring).

Robin, D.P., and R. E. Reidenbach. (1987) Social responsibility, ethics and marketing: Closing the gap between concept and application. *Journal of Marketing*, 51 (January), 44-58.

Sears, Andrew, A. Jacko Julie and Michael S. Borella (1997) Internet Delay Effects: How User's Perceive Quality, Organization and Ease of Use of Information, *CHI 1997 Conference Proceedings*, 353-354, New York: ACM Press.

Stein, Lincoln D. (1998) Internet Privacy, European Style, *Web Techniques*, 3 (11), 14-17.

WEB LOG DATA

When a student picks up a magazine in someone's dorm room, no marketer knows about it. When a homemaker flips on the TV during lunch, no one knows if she looks at the commercials. Computerized processes, however, such as serving up a Web page, can easily be recorded. A Web server creates a log record every time someone accesses any file on the Web server. The record includes a date and time stamp, the name of the requested file, the domain name and IP address of the client requesting the page, the specific software client used to request the page, and the referring URL, if any, that the visitor used to access your site. These records are invaluable in determining how well your site is doing and how to improve it.

A simplified, but typical, log record might look like this:

```
joe.cerfin.com—-
[31/Dec/1999:09:02:35 -0400]
"GET /page.html HTTP/1.0"
200 2932 "http://www.x.com/x.html"
"Mozilla/4.0 [en] (Win95; I)"
```

In this example, a user sitting at a machine named joe.cerfin.com visited a certain page on December 31 at just after 9:00 a.m. The page requested by the visitor's browser software was named "page.html." The browser wished to receive the page according to version 1.0 of the HTTP protocol. The page was successfully sent, leading to a return code of 200. If the page had not been found, the return code would have been 404, a number you may have seen when you misspelled the URL for a page you were trying to access. The server sent 2,932 bytes to the browser. Next you can see that the visitor was referred to this page—page.html—from the URL: http://www.x.com/x.html. In other words, there was a link to page.html at this second URL. The visitor got to page.html by clicking on a link on http://www.x.com/x.html. Finally, at the end of the log record information is provided indicating which browser the visitor used. In this case, the visitor used Netscape Navigator, which originally went by the nickname Mozilla, running under Windows 95.

A log record such as the one above is usually called a **hit**. There would be a separate log record for every file requested by a visitor. So if page.html had two embedded images in it, each one of those images would have generated a separate log entry. Simply counting log records, or hits, produces an overestimation of how many people saw your pages. In fact, you notice from the sample log record that there is really no information about who looked at this page. We have a better idea of the hardware and software used by the visitor than of who the visitor is. The same person can visit your site from two different domain names if they redial their Internet connection, or the same domain name could actually be two different visitors.

A related problem is that not all hits come from people. Search sites often use what are called **robots** and **spiders** to look for new pages. The browser field described above can be used to filter out these software visitors from your log files.

Another log file complication comes from use of **cache**. Cache refers to a local storage of a page. The visitor's browser saves a visited page on that person's hard drive. When you use your back arrow, instead of retrieving the page again from the server, it is quickly read from the hard drive, saving time. So usually multiple views of the same page generate a single hit unless the visitor uses the reload button. Internet service providers sometimes also cache pages for their clients to save time and processing power. This can reduce the number of hits logged.

We also need to keep in mind that just because a page was requested, that doesn't mean the visitor saw it. The visitor might change his or her mind before the page is received and use the stop sign button or the back arrow.

Nonetheless, it is possible to identify and approximately count unique visitors by making certain assumptions. One popular rule is to identify a unique visitor to a Web site by assuming that all hits from the same domain name within a 30-minute period come from the same individual. Using this definition it is possible to estimate the number of unique visitors who request the page. You can also determine your most and least popular pages.

The "referring URL" in the hit record is one way of seeing how your traffic is finding its way to your site. Does it come from search engines or other pages? What types of key words on search engines yield a reference to your site?

The referring URL in the hit record also allows you to figure out which of your pages are the most common entry and exit points. You can count how many pages people look at and get a feel for how they traverse the site, and how long the spend while they're there.

By looking at the error code 404 records, you can also see the typos people make when they are trying to find one of your pages. If a lot of potential visitors are typing in "page.htm" (without the last "L"), you might want to add a page with that name and point them in the right direction.

Studying the answers to these questions give feedback to the content site Webmaster for making improvements to the site.

Web Experiments

This text presents a large amount of information on how to create banners, pages, and sites in order to promote the goals of the organization. For a promotional site, you want a large audience of targeted visitors. Once a visitor is on your site, you want to build a close relationship with him and to engage in as much communication as possible. For a selling site, you seek a steady stream of qualified visitors. As the visitors work their way from the home page to the page in which they actually buy your product, how many of them click through and keep going at each step? The criteria most important when you manage a selling site are **conversion efficiency** or **click-through percentage**. For a content or utility site, you want a broad audience to come to your site and to look at as many pages—and be exposed to as many ads—as possible. Here the criterion is the total number of clicks. We might call this **navigational depth** or **site depth.**

There are a large number of factors that can influence your ability to achieve any of these goals. Choice of artwork, page layout, page or link copy, colors, menu structure, presence or lack of navigational aides, and even font sizes could all have an impact on time-on-site, click-through percentage, or site depth. But how do you really know whether a change to your site will be beneficial in terms of one of these goals? Since the Web server logs all of the relevant information, it is a relatively simple matter to find out empirically using a Web experiment.

Live experiments on the Web have major advantages over laboratory experiments. For one thing, the experimental "subjects" are actual visitors who are arriving on your site. The sample is the audience at the time the experiment is being run. The experiment can be performed transparently to the visitor. These factors provide excellent external validity. Thus, your results will be highly applicable to your site since they were discovered on your actual site. You can also run an experiment easily using some modest CGI programming, a topic described in Chapter 14 and discussed further below.

Page Experiments

Suppose you are trying to decide between page version A and page version B. Perhaps version A is your original home page and version B represents a design that you came up with that you hope will increase the number of links that visitors click on. Similarly, the decision could be short-term, say, which of two headlines to use for today's version of your online newsletter. You might wish to run an experiment for the first hour of the morning to see which wording to use for the rest of the day.

There are two ways to create an experiment with these two pages. If this is the home page within a directory, or the home page of your entire site, you can replace the file index.html with a CGI script. The script can generate a random number, decide which version of the page to show the visitor, and then log which version of the page it showed to the visitor. This log can then be correlated later with the normal page log for your site so that you can tell how well each version of the page did.

Another way to go about this is to have a background job that runs every 20 minutes. Assume the page in question is called x.html, and you have two versions of this page, A and B. The job could work like this:

```
copy a.html to x.html

copy b.html to a.html

copy x.html to b.html
```

If you study these statements, you will see that when the batch job is rerun 20 minutes later, a.html and b.html are reversed back again. Every 24 hours you could reverse a.html and b.html one extra time so that each one is featured in a different 20-minute period than the day before. The reverse of the reversing then completely counterbalances the experiment.

To make sure you uniquely identify which visitor saw which page, create a single pixel transparent gif called a.gif and place it at the end of a.html. Likewise, do the same for b.html using a tiny gif called b.gif.

Banner Ad Studies

An ad banner is simply a clickable image file embedded in the page. The image markup can be used to point to a program instead of an actual banner, as in

```
<IMG SRC="/cgi-bin/banner-randomizer.cgi">
```

You can have the program generate a random number, send off one of the banners in the experiment based on this random number, and then record which visitor had requested the banner and which banner you sent.

Summary

1.   It is possible to identify unique visitors to a Web site.
2.   You can run experiments to determine which version of a page or banner works the best.

Online Activities

Visit the companion Web site at www.wiley.com/college/hofacker for chapter summaries, examples, hypertext cases, homework assignments, text material updates, research exercises, and *Wall Street Journal Interactive Edition* access.

GO TO   http://www.wiley.com/college/hofacker

 THE WALL STREET JOURNAL.

References

Hanson, Ward A. and Daniel S. Putler (1997) Hits and Misses: Herd Behavior and Online Product Popularity, *Marketing Letters*, 7 (4).

Bellman, Steven and John R. Rossiter (1997) A Proposed Model for Explaining and Measuring Web Ad Effectiveness, Australian Graduate School of Management Working Paper No. 97-020.

Donato, Paul J. (1996) Research in a World of Expanding Media Options: Chicken or Egg? *Journal of Advertising Research,* (January/February), 35-42.

Berthon, Pierre; Pitt, Leyland F. and Watson, Richard T. (1996) The World Wide Web as an Advertising Medium: Toward an Understanding of Conversion Efficiency, *Journal of Advertising Research* 36 (January/February), 43-53.

Novak, Thomas P. and Donna L. Hoffman (1997) New Metrics for New Media: Toward the Development of Web Measurement Standards, *World Wide Web Journal*, 2 (Winter), 213-246.

Olson, G. M., J. D. Herbsleb and H. H. Reuter (1994). Characterizing the Sequential Structure of Interactive Behaviors through Statistical and Grammatical Techniques. *Human-Computer Interaction,* 9 (3/4), 427-472.

Sen, Shahana, Blaji Padmanabhan, Alexander Tuzhilin, Norman H. White and Roger Stein (1998) The Identification and Satisfaction of Consumer Analysis-Driven Information Needs of Marketers on the WWW, *European Journal of Marketing,* 32 (7/8), 688-702.

Stout, Rick.(1997) *Web Site Stats*. Berkeley: Osborne McGraw-Hill, 1997.

Part V

NEW FUNCTIONS, NEW BUSINESSES

Chapter 19

THE DIGITAL FUTURE

LEARNING OBJECTIVES

1. Understand the use of the Internet in making markets, a phenomenon that is typical of the Internet.
2. Understand the three main trends affecting the Internet: the growth of computing power, the number of devices being added to the network, and the increase in the bandwidth of Internet communications.

Market Making

Previous chapters have discussed using the Internet to provide content. In this section we discuss a special type of content site in which the owners of the site do not actually provide all, or even most, of the content. Consider one of the early successful Internet businesses, Yahoo!. What did the owners of Yahoo! actually do? They created an organized menu for Web sites, publicized it, and then sat back while the owners of numerous other Web sites registered their URLs. Yahoo! leveraged the desire of webmasters to get their sites in front of people. These webmasters were perfectly willing to perform work for Yahoo!, entering the URL, suggesting categories for the URL, and so forth.

Yahoo! and many other sites take advantage of the self-organizing capacity of the virtual economy. In many cases, all that is needed is for a public space to be created and to become well-known. Creating such a space facilitates the exchange between readers and writers, or buyers and sellers. The sponsoring site is helping to "make the market." Another good example is www.ebay.com. e-Bay allows individuals to sell to or buy from each other—in effect e-Bay creates a virtual garage sale running 24 hours a day. Buyers and sellers simply register with e-Bay and they are ready to trade.

The eBay site in particular, and Web commerce in general have much in common with classified ads, which are widely used to match up buyers and sellers.

Like classified ads, the Web is a pull medium that can be easily used for time-dependent information. The Web has advantages over classifieds in that it allows extensive searching and sorting and multimedia ad-ons.

In theory, sites could offer a wide variety of market-making—something we can expect to see in the near future. Such services could include the introduction of buyers and sellers, assisting where the product or service is highly specialized, creating advertising pools for sellers, helping with negotiations and terms, and providing a facility for secure or anonymous transactions.

Sites engaged in making markets tend to see an increasing return to scale. For a seller, it makes sense to use the site with the largest number of buyers. For a buyer, it makes sense to browse a site with the largest number and variety of sellers. A huge **pioneer advantage** therefore is already emerging in this area with the first Web sites well-known for making markets getting bigger and bigger.

Environmental Scanning and Market Research

The Web can be used to perform marketing research on any physical product or service. You can also use the Web for research on how to improve the Web site itself. In these cases, you can create chat-based **focus groups**—a geographically dispersed group providing feedback on a new product concept, or on changes to an older product or to the Web site. You can also use forms and CGI to create an online questionnaire (although achieving a random or representative sample online is very difficult). Another technique used by companies is to bring users into a laboratory and watch them as they navigate a Web site. Observing real users and modifying the site accordingly is called **usability engineering**.

Three Key Trends

To understand where the Internet is going, we need to contemplate three related trends. First, computing power has been doubling every 18 months or so going back for many decades. Second, the number of computers attached to the Internet has been doubling every two years. Third, bandwidth, the number of bits that can be transmitted each second has been steadily increasing, especially in the last five years.

Computing Power

Back in 1965, Gordon Moore, a cofounder of the Intel Corporation, noted that the number of transistors that fit on a single computer chip seemed to be doubling every 18 months. This rate of increase has held for many decades now, and is now called "Moore's Law." The importance of Moore's Law is that the number of transistors on a chip provides a rough sense for how powerful the computer powered by the chip is. Yesterday's supercomputer becomes today's departmental server and ultimately tomorrow's desktop machine. A new PC might have been used three years ago to run a small business or a department of a larger company. Perhaps even three years earlier a firm might have used your machine as its primary mainframe. Six or so years before that—12 years ago—supercomputers in university and government labs would have had similar speed, memory, and disk storage of a standard PC of today. Assuming Moore's Law holds, the implication is that in about 12 years you will have today's supercomputer on your desktop.

The analogy between a desktop machine and a supercomputer is somewhat strained. Supercomputers are used to model the atmosphere, nuclear detonations, and other complex processes and let scientists visualize the result. It is unclear what that sort of processing power and memory will be used for on a desktop. Perhaps it will be high-definition video, simulations of human interaction, or other applications yet to be imagined by the software designers of the next 12 years.

As a corollary to Moore's Law, as desktop machines get more powerful, the chips of the sort that power older models end up being inexpensive commodities that can be put into any product, like a credit card or a toy. Look at the Table 19.1, illustrating this point.

Computing Power	Three Years Ago	Now	Three Years from Now
1	Toy		
10	desktop computer	toy	
100	dept. server	desktop computer	toy
1,000	mainframe	dept. server	desktop computer
10,000	supercomputer	mainframe	dept. server
100,000		supercomputer	mainframe
1,000,000			supercomputer

Table 19.1–Growth of Computing Power

Devices Attached to the Internet

Another important trend is the number of devices that are attached to the Internet. Here note that we do not use the word "computer." Instead, we use the word devices. As discussed above, intelligent processors are being found in more and more things around the home, from cars, refrigerators, CD players, and ovens—all the way down to talking dolls. Now that IP has become the universal language for connecting intelligent processors, we should expect more and more of these devices to become interconnected. You might wonder why anyone would connect a doll to the Internet. Perhaps an educational software company could use IP to load grammar lessons into the doll that would get increasingly difficult as the child grows older. Or imagine the delight of a child when the doll might introduce itself to a brand new toy from the same company that was just brought home that day.

A network with one computer is not a useful network, but once there are two computers, things get interesting. Robert Metcalf, who invented Ethernet and founded 3Com, has articulated a law that states how the value of a network increases as more people use it. Metcalf's Law holds that the value of a network is a function of the square of the number of computers attached to it.

Metcalf's Law is related to what economists call an **externality**. An externality is a consequence not accounted for by a market price. In some cases externalities can be negative, as might be argued is the case when the price of gasoline does not reflect the cost of pollution, congestion, or the cost of militarily protecting the oil supply. In the case of the Internet, the externalities are positive, since whenever someone else connects to the Internet, everyone else's connection becomes that much more valuable.

Like computing power, the number of attached devices doubles during a fixed amount of time. Linear change might look like 10 in the first year, 20 in the second year, 30 in the third year, and so forth. Instead, since the number of attached computers tends to double in a fixed amount of time, we describe this as exponential increase. So instead of adding the number 10 from one year to the next, we multiply by 10. See Figure 19.1 for an illustration of this growth.

When you add Metcalf's Law on top of this exponential growth, you can see that the Internet is becoming more valuable very rapidly.

Bandwidth

Now we have Moore's Law describing chip capability and Metcalf's Law describing the utility of a network increasing with the square of the number of attached machines. Is there a law for bandwidth? Andy Grove, the former CEO of Intel, once joked that phone company bandwidth doubled every 100 years. He was not being entirely serious, but his comment does make the point that the

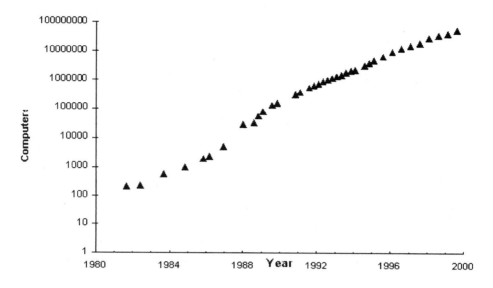

Figure 19.1

Matthew Gray of the Massachusetts Institute of Technology measured the growth of the number of host computers connected to the Internet between 1993 and 1996, during which time the number of Internet host computers increased 600 percent.

capacity to send information from one computer to another has not grown as fast as some other aspects of information technology. This area has been hindered by the local monopoly held by phone companies in various regions of the world.

Now some analysts expect bandwidth to begin to increase quickly as well. Already in the past 10 years modem speeds have gone from 1,200 bits per second to 56,000—adding a zero and then some. Cable modems are coming online now that can provide 10 millions bits per second of bandwidth. It is conceivable that phone companies may actually begin to market new high-speed digital subscriber lines to consumers, although their track record for such innovations has not been sterling.

Nevertheless, assume for the moment that computing power—the number of computers attached to the Internet—and bandwidth all keep growing at the present rate. Using this method, extrapolate out to 2007. At that time you would have an Internet consisting of around one billion devices. Each of these would be about as powerful as today's mainframes. They would be interconnected at a rate of speed that would allow High Definition TV (HDTV) quality video.

By then, the Internet will have rapidly taken over the telephone network, followed by radio, followed by television. This is not to say that there will no longer be telephones, radios, or TVs. Communication for these devices will be IP-based, and these devices will have computers in them. The media environment for TV and radio will presumably be more Web-like then, with millions of "stations" having global reach, and with the visitor having a higher level of control than today.

High-quality video connections will accelerate many of the trends discussed in this book. Humans are very good at reading each other when they share a common culture. Video will further empower small groups regardless of location.

Video will also make possible many services that are not possible today. Cameras will be placed at intersections, freeway overpasses, and parking lots so that you can assess your commute to work. The security business will be transformed as public spaces will receive routine video coverage. In addition, new forms of entertainment will become prevalent as digital cameras fall in price. In general, new forms of human interaction will be created, enabling new forms of group action. A prototype might be the "SETI on the desktop" project. Participants can download a screen saver that will direct their computer to help process radio waves from telescopes, when they are not using it.

We might guess that as more of the economy is "virtualized," prices will remain moderate with little inflation.

Software agents will be able to do your shopping legwork. Already there are prototype programs that can go off on the network, search for the best deal, and report back to you.

Before we conclude that we know what the future will be, it is important to step back and take a deep breath. Biologists have a pretty good idea how each cell in your body functions. Even so, it is quite impossible for a biologist to predict what you will eat for lunch today. The collection of cells that comprise your body has **emergent properties**. Systems that are created from numerous different pieces have properties that do not emerge in a predictable way from the properties of their constituent parts. The Internet is likely to have some emergent properties that we can't even speculate about now. Thus, it will be important for marketing organizations to remain flexible. The ability to react with agility will be more important than guessing right about the future.

Summary

1.   Computing power and the size of the Internet are growing exponentially, not linearly.

2.   The Internet will likely reveal emergent properties in the future that are not apparent today.

3.   Firms need to be able to react with agility to the challenges that the Internet will bring to the competitive environment.

Online Activities

Visit the companion Web site at www.wiley.com/college/hofacker for chapter summaries, examples, hypertext cases, homework assignments, text material updates, research exercises, and *Wall Street Journal Interactive Edition* access.

GO TO   http://www.wiley.com/college/hofacker

 THE WALL STREET JOURNAL.

References

Anderson, Susan E. and Bruce M. Gansneder (1995) Using Electronic Mail Surveys and Computer-Monitored Data for Studying Computer Mediated Commnication Systems, *Social Science Computer Review*, 13 (Spring), 33-46.

Arthur, W. Brian (1996) Increasing Returns and the New World of Business, *Harvard Business Review*, July-August, 100-109.

Edmondson, Brad (1997) The Wired Bunch: Online Surveys and Focus Groups Might Solve the Toughest Problems in Market Research, But Can the Internet Really Speak for Everyone? *American Demographics*, 19 (June), 10-15.

Forrest, Edward (1999) *Internet Marketing Research: Resources and Techniques*, Roseville NSW 2069, Australia: McGraw Hill Companies.

Gaiser, Ted J. (1997) Conducting On-line Focus Groups: A Methodological Discussion, *Social Science Computing Review*, 15 (Summer), 135-144.

Hamlin, Charlie (1997) Market Research and the Wired Consumer, *Marketing News*, 31 (June), 6.

Ives, Blake and Sirkka L. Jarvenpaa (1996) Will the Internet Revolutionize Business Education and Research? *Sloan Management Review*, (Spring), 33-41.

Kiesler, Sara and Lee S. Sproull (1986) Response Effects in the Electronic Survey, *Public Opinion Quarterly*, 50, 402-413.

King, Wesley C. Jr. and Edward W. Miles (1995) A Quasi-Experimental Assessment of the Effect of Computerizing Concognitive Paper-and-Pencil Measurements: A Test of Measurement Equivalence, *Journal of Applied Psychology*, 80 (6), 643-651.

Mehta, R. and E. Sivadas. (1995) Comparing response rates and response content in mail versus electronic mail surveys. *Journal of the Market Research Society*, 37 (4), 429-446.

Montoya-Weiss, Mitzi M., Anne P. Massey and Danial L. Clapper (1998) On-Line Focus Groups: Conceptual Issues and a Research Tool, *European Journal of Marketing,* 32 (7/8), 713-723.

Oppermann, Martin (1995) E-Mail Surveys: Potential and Pitfalls, *Marketing Research*, 7 (Summer), 28-33.

Petrecca, Laura (1997) Research Web Mines the Net for Effective Survey Results, *Advertising Age*, July 21.

Schonland, Addison M. and Peter W. Williams (1996) Using the Internet for Travel and Tourism Survey Research: Experiences from the Net Traveler Survey, *Journal of Travel Research*, 35 (2), 81-87.

Schuldt, Barbara A. and Jeff W. Totten (1994) Electronic Mail vs. Mail Survey Response Rates, *Marketing Research*, 6 (Winter), 36-39.

Tse, Alan, Ka Chun Tse, Chow Hoi Yin, and Choy Ting (1995) Comparing Two Methods of Sending Out Questionnaires: E-mail Versus Mail, *Journal of the Marketing Research Society*, 37 (4), 441-446.

Sahay, Arvind, Jane Gould and Patrick Barwise (1998) New Interactive Media: Experts' Perceptions of Opportunities and Threats for Existing Businesses, *European Journal of Marketing*, 32 (7/8), 616-628.

Shapiro, Carl and Hal Varian (1998) *Information Rules: A Strategic Guide to the Network Economy*, Boston: Harvard Business School Press.

GLOSSARY

Address for the list   An email address associated with an email list that is used for administrative purposes such as subscribing or unsubscribing to the list.

Address for the server   An email address associated with an email list. If you send email to this address, each subscriber to the email list receives your note.

ASCII   A method for representing text in a document. ASCII is the simplest way of creating text.

Asynchronous communication   Communication in which both parties do not have to be engaged at the same time.

Attention   A limited capacity human system where some information is processed while other information is ignored.

Authentication   The ability to determine the identity of a computer user.

Bandwidth   The capability or speed of a communications channel measured in the number of bits per second that can be sent or received.

Body copy   The main block of copy on a Web site or in an advertisement.

Brand risk   The risk to a consumer that a certain brand might prove unsatisfactory.

Central route   A method of persuasion based on logical arguments.

Click through   The act of clicking on an image or link to call up a different document.

Click through pricing   A system for charging for ad banners based on how many people click on the ad and visit the advertiser's site.

Client   Software that requests a network service.

Compensatory comparison   A method consumers use to evaluate products in which a good score on one product characteristic can compensate for a bad score on some other characteristic.

Comprehension   A connection between an input on the screen and something previously stored in the consumers mind.

Confidentiality   The ability to send a message that will only be readable by the intended recipient.

Convenience goods   Products which are purchased wherever available.

Conversion efficiency   The probability that a visitor will click on a key link on a page.

Cookies   Data exchanged between a Web client and server allowing the server to track visitor activities.

Copy   The text appearing on a Web site or ad.

CPM pricing   A system for charging for ad banners based on how many people visit the page on which the banner resides.

Credence characteristics   Product attributes that cannot ever be evaluated.

Digital signature   A way to ascertain the identity of a message sender.

Disintermediation   The capability of the Internet to eliminate channel members and to do directly to consumers instead.

Domain Name System   A distributed method of letting one device find out the network address of another.

Electronic hierarchy   Business to business Internet marketing in which one firm is dominant.

Electronic mail   A mechanism to send text and other material from one user to another using a store and forward principle.

Electronic market   Business to business Internet marketing where a number of firms compete to sell services to each other.

Elimination Rules   A method consumers use to evaluate products in which a product must meet some minimum criterion on some characteristics.

Email list   A mechanism to send email to multiple recipients at once. Email lists are often organized around a topic of interest to those who subscribe to the list.

Emergent properties   Properties of a complex system that cannot be inferred from the properties of the component parts of that system.

Experience characteristics   Product attributes that can be evaluated after purchase.

Exposure   The act of viewing or hearing a message.

Firewall   A system allowing a firm to filter network traffic that is coming into or going out of a local system.

Flame   Posting an email message negative or hostile in tone.

Flat ad   The simplest type of communications Web site that resembles an online brochure.

Flow   An optimal psychological experience occurring when there is a match between the challenge at hand and one's skills.

Frequently asked question   Many of the technical questions that come up on the Internet are FAQs, or frequently asked questions. Often these FAQs are collected in a document for newcomers.

Frictionless transaction   The capability of the Internet to reduce the cost of doing business for buyers and sellers.

Hedonic surfers   Web visitors who are looking for entertainment by "consuming" a site.

Hyperlink   Part of the screen that can be clicked on to bring up related information.

Hypertext   Nonlinear text in which part of the document is live and lets you link to related documents.

Hypertext Markup Language   The computer code used to create Web documents.

Information intermediary   The capability of the Internet to create new channels members that facilitate the flow of information in markets.

Information space   The collection of information on a Web site and how the different pieces of information relate to and are connected with each other.

Interactive marketing   Customized online communications that takes into account previous input from the consumer.

Interactive medium   A communications channel in which consumers control communication patterns.

Internet   The sum total of all devices interconnected using the internet protocol.

Internet Protocol   A set of technical agreements allowing devices to communicate.

Internet Relay Chat   A real time, or synchronous, method of conversation by typing.

IP spoofing   Pretending to be from a different address than your true address.

Keyboard sniffing   A virus program that captures keystrokes on a PC.

Local Area Network   A set of hardware connections between computers in a small geographical regions such as the floor of a building.

Marketing site   A communications Web site designed to create relationships with consumers, or to allow consumers to enter into communications relationships with each other.

Mass customization   The ability to produce unique responses for a large number of consumers.

Mass medium   A communications channel in which firms control communication patterns.

Menu bar   The second line of a window with a set of words on it. Clicking on a word invokes a menu of options.

Metcalf's law   The usefulness of a network increases with the square of the number of users of that network.

Mode razor   A design philosophy in which the rules for how to use software do not change.

Moderated email list   An email list where the postings are controlled by a gatekeeper known as a moderator.

Moore's law   The number of transistors that can be fit on a chip doubles every 18 months.

Navigation   The process by which a consumer moves from one page to another on the Web.

Navigational depth   The number of pages visited on a Web site by visitors. Navigation depth is also called site depth.

Nesting   Items appearing within, or as part of, other items.

Netiquette   A set of cultural do's and don'ts that define polite behavior on the Internet.

Newsgroup   A newsgroup is part of Usenet and consists of a collection of postings on a particular subject.

Open protocol   Technical specifications not owned by any individual or company.

Packet routing   A system of computer communication in which messages are broken into pieces and each piece makes its own way to the destination.

Packet sniffing   A program that captures all of the information travelling on a certain segment of a network.

Perception   The act of making a connection between a screen input and something stored in the consumers mind.

Peripheral route   A method of persuasion based on feeling.

Points   The size of a typeface. There are 72 points to an inch.

Prima facie duties   An ethical framework that assumes there are a set of duties that constitute inherent moral obligations.

Privacy risk   The risk to a consumer that information entered on the Internet might end up in the wrong company's or person's hands.

Private key   One of a matched set of keys that can encode or decode messages in public key cryptography. What the public key encodes only the private key can decode, and vice versa.

Proportionality   An ethical approach that considers the intention, the means, and the ends for a decision. Negative unintended consequences may be risked only if the means and ends are good, and there is a proportionate reason for taking the risk.

Proprietary protocol   Technical specifications owned by a company.

Public key   One of a matched set of keys that can encode or decode messages in public key cryptography. What the public key encodes only the private key can decode, and vice versa.

Public key cryptography   A mechanism for authenticating users and providing confidentiality over an insecure network like the Internet.

Pull   Commercial communication initiated by consumers.

Pure competition   A theoretical economic state with numerous sellers and where each buyer has full information on all sellers.

Push   Commercial communication that is forced on consumers, or intrudes on them.

Race condition   An attempt to beat server information to the client.

Retention   The ability to remember previously stored information.

Revisit   The number of visitors to a Web site who return later.

Robots   Software that accesses Web pages automatically, without a human browser.

Runner   A part of the screen set aside for some purpose, usually highlighted with a different background color.

Schema   An organized collection of information about the world with many embedded parts.

Search characteristics   Product attributes that can be evaluated during shopping.

Security risk   The risk that a consumer's credit card might become compromised as a result of paying for an item on the Internet.

Serif   Cross lines that appear on certain typefaces such as Times Roman.

Server   Software that provides a network service.

Session hijacking   A technique allowing a remote user to take over someone's terminal session.

Shopping goods   Products which inspire consumers to do research on the brands in the category.

Shout   Posting an email message in all uppercase characters.

Sig file   Several lines appearing at the end of an email message identifying the sender, often providing some information about the sender's company.

Site depth   The number of pages visited on a Web site by visitors. Site depth is also called navigational depth.

Spam   Unsolicited email sent for a commercial purpose.

Specialty goods   Products which engender brand loyalty and for which a consumer would be willing to search for an outlet carrying their favorite brand.

Spiders   Software that traverses from one Web page to another, looking for links to add to search engine sites.

Strong encryption   The ability to achieve unbreakable confidentiality.

Time risk   The risk to a consumer that a visit to a site might be a waste of time.

Title bar   The top line of a window such as a window for a Web browser.

Tool bar   The third line of a window with shortcuts for some of the menu bar options.

Trademark   A trademark is any word, name, symbol or used to identify a firm.

Trial   The number of first time visitors to a Web site.

Typeface   A style or appearance of lettering.

Uniform Resource Locator   An address of a document or object on the World Wide Web.

Unmoderated email list   An email list where postings occur automatically with no gatekeeper.

Usability engineering   Observing real users and modifying the site accordingly is called usability engineering.

Usenet   A system of "bulletin board" interest groups on thousands of different topics.

Utilitarian ethics   An ethical approach that looks for the decision alternative that produces the greatest good for the greatest number of people.

Utilitarian searchers   Web visitors with a work-like mentality who are looking for specific information.

Vendor risk   The risk to a consumer that a site might be designed to rip them off.

Virtual buying pool   A cooperative collection of buyers who band together for the best deal.

Virtual community   A set of consumers who often communicate with each other.

Virtual segment   A geographically dispersed collection of consumers with similar tastes.

Virtual space   Computer and network hardware given over to use by consumers for the purpose of allowing them to communicate with each other.

Weight   The heaviness or boldness of a typeface.

World Wide Web   A client server system using hypertext.

WYSIWYG   An acronym standing for What You See Is What You Get. Some page creator software works this way.

Yielding   Agreeing with a message and accepting its arguments or position.

INDEX